Why So Few?

Women in Science, Technology, Engineering, and Mathematics

Catherine Hill, Ph.D.   Christianne Corbett   Andresse St. Rose, Ed.D.

AAUW

Published by AAUW
1111 Sixteenth St. NW
Washington, DC 20036
Phone: 202/728-7602
Fax: 202/463-7169
E-mail: connect@aauw.org
Web: www.aauw.org

First printing: February 2010

Library of Congress Control Number: 2010901076
ISBN: 978-1-879922-40-2

077-10 5M 02/10

Cover: Esther Ngumbi, 2007–08 AAUW International Fellow; photo by the University of Idaho
Photography Department

This report was made possible by the generous contributions of

The National Science Foundation,

The Letitia Corum Memorial Fund,

The Mooneen Lecce Giving Circle, and

The Eleanor Roosevelt Fund

The Letitia Corum Memorial Fund honors the legacy of

Letitia Corum

whose commitment to AAUW continues to inspire advocacy and research on the issues that matter in the lives of women and girls.

The Mooneen Lecce Giving Circle provides support for programs that advance equity for women and girls.

AAUW acknowledges the financial support of the National Science Foundation, Gender in Science and Engineering Division, grant 0832982, for the production and dissemination of this report. Any opinions, findings, and conclusions or recommendations expressed in this material are those of the authors and do not necessarily reflect the views of the National Science Foundation.

Table of Contents

Foreword ——————————————————————————— ix

Acknowledgments ——————————————————— x

About the Authors ——————————————————— xii

Executive Summary ——————————————————— xiii

Chapter 1.   Women and Girls in Science, Technology,
             Engineering, and Mathematics ——————— 1

Chapter 2.   Beliefs about Intelligence ——————————— 29

Chapter 3.   Stereotypes ——————————————————— 37

Chapter 4.   Self-Assessment ——————————————— 43

Chapter 5.   Spatial Skills ——————————————————— 51

Chapter 6.   The College Student Experience ——————— 57

Chapter 7.   University and College Faculty ——————— 67

Chapter 8.   Implicit Bias ——————————————————— 73

Chapter 9.   Workplace Bias ——————————————— 81

Chapter 10. Recommendations ——————————————— 89

Bibliography ——————————————————————— 97

Table of Figures

Figure 1.   High School Credits Earned in Mathematics and Science, by Gender, 1990–2005 ——— 4

Figure 2.   Grade Point Average in High School Mathematics and Science (Combined), by Gender, 1990–2005 ——— 4

Figure 3.   Students Taking Advanced Placement Tests in Mathematics and Science, by Gender, 2009 ——— 6

Figure 4.   Average Scores on Advanced Placement Tests in Mathematics and Science Subjects, by Gender, 2009 ——— 7

Figure 5.   Intent of First-Year College Students to Major in STEM Fields, by Race-Ethnicity and Gender, 2006 ——— 8

Figure 6.   Bachelor's Degrees Earned by Women in Selected Fields, 1966–2006 ——— 9

Figure 7.   Bachelor's Degrees Earned in Selected Science and Engineering Fields, by Gender, 2007 ——— 10

Figure 8.   Bachelor's Degrees Earned by Underrepresented Racial-Ethnic Groups in Selected STEM Fields, by Gender, 2007 ——— 11

Figure 9.   Doctorates Earned by Women in Selected STEM Fields, 1966–2006 ——— 12

Figure 10. Women in Selected STEM Occupations, 2008 ——— 14

Figure 11. Women in Selected STEM Occupations, 1960–2000 ——— 15

Figure 12a. Workers with Doctorates in the Computer and Information Sciences Workforce, by Gender and Employment Status, 2006 ——— 16

Figure 12b. Workers with Doctorates in the Biological, Agricultural, and Environmental Life Science Workforce, by Gender and Employment Status, 2006 ——— 16

Figure 13. Female STEM Faculty in Four-Year Educational
            Institutions, by Discipline and Tenure Status, 2006 ——————— 18

Figure 14. A Fixed versus a Growth Mindset ——————— 32

Figure 15. Performance on a Challenging Math Test, by Stereotype
            Threat Condition and Gender ——————— 40

Figure 16. Self-Assessment of Ability, by Gender ——————— 48

Figure 17. Students' Standards for Their Own Performance, by
            Gender ——————— 49

Figure 18. Sample Question from the Purdue Spatial Visualization
            Test: Rotations (PSVT:R) ——————— 54

Figure 19. Process for Improving Recruitment and Retention of
            Women in Computer Science ——————— 62

Figure 20. Instructions for an Implicit Association Test on Gender
            and Science ——————— 75

Figure 21. Competence and Likability for Women and Men in
            "Male" Professions ——————— 84

Foreword

AAUW is proud to have been selected by the National Science Foundation to conduct this study of women's underrepresentation in science, technology, engineering, and mathematics. Since 1881, AAUW has encouraged women to study and work in these areas through fellowships and grants, research, programming, and advocacy. From local science camps and conferences to our groundbreaking research reports, AAUW has a long history of breaking through barriers for women and girls.

Women have made tremendous progress in education and the workplace during the past 50 years. Even in historically male fields such as business, law, and medicine, women have made impressive gains. In scientific areas, however, women's educational gains have been less dramatic, and their progress in the workplace still slower. In an era when women are increasingly prominent in medicine, law, and business, why are so few women becoming scientists and engineers?

This study tackles this puzzling question and presents a picture of what we know—and what is still to be understood—about girls and women in scientific fields. The report focuses on practical ways that families, schools, and communities can create an environment of encouragement that can disrupt negative stereotypes about women's capacity in these demanding fields. By supporting the development of girls' confidence in their ability to learn math and science, we help motivate interest in these fields. Women's educational progress should be celebrated, yet more work is needed to ensure that women and girls have full access to educational and employment opportunities in science, technology, engineering, and mathematics.

Carolyn H. Garfein
AAUW President

Linda D. Hallman
AAUW Executive Director

Acknowledgments

AAUW is deeply grateful to the scholars whose work is profiled in the report: Joshua Aronson, Mahzarin Banaji, Shelley Correll, Carol Dweck, Allan Fisher, Madeline Heilman, Jane Margolis, Sheryl Sorby, Cathy Trower, and Barbara Whitten.

AAUW thanks its staff and member leaders for their contributions. In particular AAUW is grateful for the exceptional work of Jill Birdwhistell, chief of strategic advancement; Rebecca Lanning, director of publications; Allison VanKanegan, designer; and Susan K. Dyer, consultant and editor.

Finally, AAUW thanks the members of its distinguished research advisory committee for their guidance. Special thanks go to Ruta Sevo for her work on the conceptual stage of the project and her substantive comments on early drafts of the report.

ADVISORY COMMITTEE

- **Barbara Bogue**, co-founder and director of the Assessing Women and Men in Engineering (AWE) Project, associate professor of engineering science and mechanics, and director of the Women in Engineering Program, College of Engineering, Penn State University

- **Meg A. Bond**, professor of psychology and director of the Center for Women and Work, University of Massachusetts, Lowell, and resident scholar at the Brandeis University Women's Studies Research Center

- **Carol J. Burger**, associate professor, Department of Interdisciplinary Studies, Virginia Tech, and founder and editor of the *Journal of Women and Minorities in Science and Engineering*

- **Joanne McGrath Cohoon**, assistant professor, Department of Science, Technology, and Society, University of Virginia, and senior research scientist at the National Center for Women & IT (NCWIT)

- **Margaret Eisenhart**, University Distinguished Professor and Charles Professor of Education, School of Education, University of Colorado, Boulder

- **T. Lynn Fountain**, principal research scientist, Signature Technology Laboratory, Georgia Tech Research Institute; past president and vice president-program, AAUW of Georgia; and past president of the AAUW Atlanta (GA) Branch

- **Barbara Gault**, executive director and vice president, Institute for Women's Policy Research

- **Yolanda S. George**, deputy director of education and human resources programs, American Association for the Advancement of Science

- **Gail Hackett**, provost and executive vice chancellor for academic affairs and professor of counseling and educational psychology, University of Missouri, Kansas City

- **Diane F. Halpern**, professor of psychology, Claremont McKenna College, and past president, American Psychological Association

- **Alice Hogan**, retired program director, ADVANCE program, National Science Foundation, and independent consultant for programs and policies to advance the participation of women in academic science and engineering

- **Ruta Sevo**, independent consultant and former senior program director for research on gender in science and engineering, National Science Foundation

- **Margery Sullivan**, biologist, Laboratory of Malaria Vector Research, National Institutes of Health; longtime member of AAUW; and AAUW Program Committee member

- **Karen L. Tonso**, associate professor of educational foundations, Wayne State University, and former reservoir engineer in the petroleum industry

- **Virginia Valian**, co-director of the Hunter College Gender Equity Project and Distinguished Professor of Psychology and Linguistics at Hunter College and the CUNY Graduate Center

About the Authors

CATHERINE HILL, PH.D., is the director of research at AAUW, where she focuses on higher education and women's economic security. Prior to her work at AAUW, she was a researcher at the Institute for Women's Policy Research and an assistant professor at the University of Virginia. She has bachelor's and master's degrees from Cornell University and a doctorate in public policy from Rutgers University.

CHRISTIANNE CORBETT is a research associate at AAUW and co-author of *Where the Girls Are: The Facts About Gender Equity in Education* (2008). Before coming to AAUW, she worked as a legislative fellow in the office of Rep. Carolyn Maloney and as a mechanical design engineer in the aerospace industry. She holds a master's degree in cultural anthropology from the University of Colorado, Boulder, and bachelor's degrees in aerospace engineering and government from the University of Notre Dame. As a Peace Corps volunteer in Ghana from 1992 to 1994, she taught math and science to secondary school students.

ANDRESSE ST. ROSE, ED.D., is a research associate at AAUW, where she focuses on gender equity in education and the workplace. Before joining the AAUW staff, she worked as an academic counselor at Northeastern University in Boston and taught high school math and biology at the International School of Port-of-Spain, Trinidad. She is a co-author of *Where the Girls Are: The Facts About Gender Equity in Education* (2008). She has a doctoral degree in education policy from George Washington University, a master's degree in higher education administration from Boston College, and a bachelor's degree in biology from Hamilton College.

Executive Summary

The number of women in science and engineering is growing, yet men continue to outnumber women, especially at the upper levels of these professions. In elementary, middle, and high school, girls and boys take math and science courses in roughly equal numbers, and about as many girls as boys leave high school prepared to pursue science and engineering majors in college. Yet fewer women than men pursue these majors. Among first-year college students, women are much less likely than men to say that they intend to major in science, technology, engineering, or math (STEM). By graduation, men outnumber women in nearly every science and engineering field, and in some, such as physics, engineering, and computer science, the difference is dramatic, with women earning only 20 percent of bachelor's degrees. Women's representation in science and engineering declines further at the graduate level and yet again in the transition to the workplace.

Drawing on a large and diverse body of research, this report presents eight recent research findings that provide evidence that social and environmental factors contribute to the under-representation of women in science and engineering. The rapid increase in the number of girls achieving very high scores on mathematics tests once thought to measure innate ability suggests that cultural factors are at work. Thirty years ago there were 13 boys for every girl who scored above 700 on the SAT math exam at age 13; today that ratio has shrunk to about 3:1. This increase in the number of girls identified as "mathematically gifted" suggests that education can and does make a difference at the highest levels of mathematical achievement. While biological gender differences, yet to be well understood, may play a role, they clearly are not the whole story.

Girls' Achievements and Interest in Math and Science Are Shaped by the Environment around Them

This report demonstrates the effects of societal beliefs and the learning environment on girls' achievements and interest in science and math. One finding shows that when teachers and parents tell girls that their intelligence can expand with experience and learning, girls do better on math tests and are more likely to say they want to continue to study math in the future. That is, believing in the potential for intellectual growth, in and of itself, improves outcomes. This is true for all students, but it is particularly helpful for girls in mathematics, where negative stereotypes persist about their abilities. By creating a "growth mindset" environment, teachers and parents can encourage girls' achievement and interest in math and science.

Does the stereotype that boys are better than girls in math and science still affect girls today? Research profiled in this report shows that negative stereotypes about girls' abilities in math can indeed measurably lower girls' test performance. Researchers also believe that stereotypes can lower girls' aspirations for science and engineering careers over time. When test administrators tell students that girls and boys are equally capable in math, however, the difference in performance essentially disappears, illustrating that changes in the learning environment can improve girls' achievement in math.

The issue of self-assessment, or how we view our own abilities, is another area where cultural factors have been found to limit girls' interest in mathematics and mathematically challenging careers. Research profiled in the report finds that girls assess their mathematical abilities lower than do boys with similar mathematical achievements. At the same time, girls hold themselves to a higher standard than boys do in subjects like math, believing that they have to be exceptional to succeed in "male" fields. One result of girls' lower self-assessment of their math ability—even in the face of good grades and test scores—and their higher standards for performance is that fewer girls than boys aspire to STEM careers. By emphasizing that girls and boys achieve equally well in math and science, parents and teachers can encourage girls to assess their skills more accurately.

One of the largest gender differences in cognitive abilities is found in the area of spatial skills, with boys and men consistently outperforming girls and women. Spatial skills are considered by many people to be important for success in engineering and other scientific fields. Research highlighted in this report, however, documents that individuals' spatial skills consistently improve dramatically in a short time with a simple training course. If girls grow up in an environment that enhances their success in science and math with spatial skills training, they are more likely to develop their skills as well as their confidence and consider a future in a STEM field.

At Colleges and Universities, Little Changes Can Make a Big Difference in Attracting and Retaining Women in STEM

The foundation for a STEM career is laid early in life, but scientists and engineers are made in colleges and universities. Research profiled in this report demonstrates that small improvements by physics and computer science departments, such as providing a broader overview of the field in introductory courses, can add up to big gains in female student recruitment and retention. Likewise, colleges and universities can attract more female science and engineering faculty if they improve departmental culture to promote the integration of female faculty. Research described in this report provides evidence that women are less satisfied with the academic workplace and more likely to leave it earlier in their careers than their male counterparts are. College and university administrators can recruit and retain more women by implementing mentoring programs and effective work-life policies for all faculty members.

Bias, Often Unconscious, Limits Women's Progress in Scientific and Engineering Fields

Most people associate science and math fields with "male" and humanities and arts fields with "female," according to research examined in this report. Implicit bias is common, even among individuals who actively reject these stereotypes. This bias not only affects individuals' attitudes toward others but may also influence girls' and women's likelihood of cultivating their own interest in math and science. Taking the implicit bias test at https://implicit.harvard.edu can help people identify and understand their biases so that they can work to compensate for them.

Not only are people more likely to associate math and science with men than with women, people often hold negative opinions of women in "masculine" positions, like scientists or engineers. Research profiled in this report shows that people judge women to be less competent than men in "male" jobs unless they are clearly successful in their work. When a woman is clearly competent in a "masculine" job, she is considered to be less likable. Because both likability and competence are needed for success in the workplace, women in STEM fields can find themselves in a double bind. If women and men in science and engineering know that this bias exists, they can work to interrupt the unconscious thought processes that lead to it. It may also help women specifically to know that if they encounter social disapproval in their role as a computer scientist or physicist, it is likely not personal and there are ways to counteract it.

The striking disparity between the numbers of men and women in science, technology, engineering, and mathematics has often been considered as evidence of biologically driven gender differences in abilities and interests. The classical formulation of this idea is that men "naturally" excel in mathematically demanding disciplines, whereas women "naturally" excel in fields using language skills. Recent gains in girls' mathematical achievement, however, demonstrate the importance of culture and learning environments in the cultivation of abilities and interests. To diversify the STEM fields we must take a hard look at the stereotypes and biases that still pervade our culture. Encouraging more girls and women to enter these vital fields will require careful attention to the environment in our classrooms and workplaces and throughout our culture.

Chapter 1.

Women and Girls in Science,
Technology, Engineering,
and Mathematics

Science, technology, engineering, and mathematics (STEM) are widely regarded as critical to the national economy. Concern about America's ability to be competitive in the global economy has led to a number of calls to action to strengthen the pipeline into these fields (National Academy of Sciences, Committee on Science, Engineering & Public Policy, 2007; U.S. Government Accountability Office, 2006; U.S. Department of Education, 2006). Expanding and developing the STEM workforce is a critical issue for government, industry leaders, and educators. Despite the tremendous gains that girls and women have made in education and the workforce during the past 50 years, progress has been uneven, and certain scientific and engineering disciplines remain overwhelmingly male. This report addresses why there are still so few women in certain scientific and engineering fields and provides recommendations to increase the number of women in these fields.

The National Science Foundation estimates that about five million people work directly in science, engineering, and technology—just over 4 percent of the workforce.[1] This relatively small group of workers is considered to be critical to economic innovation and productivity. Workers in science and engineering fields tend to be well paid and enjoy better job security than do other workers. Workforce projections for 2018 by the U.S. Department of Labor show that nine of the 10 fastest-growing occupations that require at least a bachelor's degree will require significant scientific or mathematical training. Many science and engineering occupations are predicted to grow faster than the average rate for all occupations, and

Definition of Science, Technology, Engineering, and Mathematics (STEM)

STEM is defined in many ways (for example, see U.S. government definitions at http://nces.ed.gov/pubs2009/2009161.pdf). In this report the term "STEM" refers to the physical, biological, and agricultural sciences; computer and information sciences; engineering and engineering technologies; and mathematics. The social and behavioral sciences, such as psychology and economics, are not included, nor are health workers, such as doctors and nurses. College and university STEM faculty are included when possible, but high school teachers in STEM subjects are not. While all of these workers are part of the larger scientific and engineering workforce, their exclusion is based on the availability of data. In this report the terms "STEM," "science, technology, engineering, and mathematics," and "scientific and engineering fields" are used interchangeably.

---

[1] Defined by occupation, the United States science and engineering workforce totaled between 4.3 and 5.8 million people in 2006. Those in science and engineering occupations who had bachelor's degrees were estimated at between 4.3 and 5.0 million. The National Science Foundation includes social scientists but not medical professionals in these estimates (National Science Board, 2010). Estimates of the size of the scientific, engineering, and technological workforce are produced using different criteria by several U.S. government agencies including the Census Bureau, the National Science Foundation, and the Bureau of Labor Statistics. Defined more broadly, the size of the STEM workforce has been estimated to exceed 21 million people.

some of the largest increases will be in engineering- and computer-related fields—fields in which women currently hold one-quarter or fewer positions (Lacey & Wright, 2009; National Science Board, 2010).

Attracting and retaining more women in the STEM workforce will maximize innovation, creativity, and competitiveness. Scientists and engineers are working to solve some of the most vexing challenges of our time—finding cures for diseases like cancer and malaria, tackling global warming, providing people with clean drinking water, developing renewable energy sources, and understanding the origins of the universe. Engineers design many of the things we use daily—buildings, bridges, computers, cars, wheelchairs, and X-ray machines. When women are not involved in the design of these products, needs and desires unique to women may be overlooked. For example, "some early voice-recognition systems were calibrated to typical male voices. As a result, women's voices were literally unheard. … Similar cases are found in many other industries. For instance, a predominantly male group of engineers tailored the first generation of automotive airbags to adult male bodies, resulting in avoidable deaths for women and children" (Margolis & Fisher, 2002, pp. 2–3). With a more diverse workforce, scientific and technological products, services, and solutions are likely to be better designed and more likely to represent all users.

The opportunity to pursue a career in science, technology, engineering, and mathematics is also a matter of pay equity. Occupational segregation accounts for the majority of the wage gap (AAUW Educational Foundation, 2007), and although women still earn less than men earn in science and engineering fields, as they do on average in the overall workforce, women in science and engineering tend to earn more than women earn in other sectors of the workforce. According to a July 2009 survey, the average starting salary for someone with a bachelor's degree in mechanical engineering, for example, was just over $59,000. By comparison, the average starting salary for an individual with a bachelor's degree in economics was just under $50,000 (National Association of Colleges and Employers, 2009).

PREPARATION OF GIRLS FOR STEM FIELDS

Math skills are considered essential to success in STEM fields. Historically, boys have outperformed girls in math, but in the past few decades the gender gap has narrowed, and today girls are doing as well as boys in math on average (Hyde et al., 2008). Girls are earning high school math and science credits at the same rate as boys and are earning slightly higher grades in these classes (U.S. Department of Education, National Center for Education Statistics, 2007) (see figures 1 and 2).

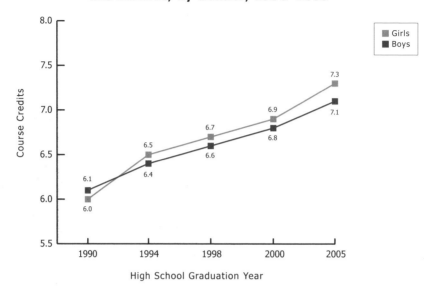

Figure 1. High School Credits Earned in Mathematics and Science, by Gender, 1990–2005

Source: U.S. Department of Education, National Center for Education Statistics, 2007, *The Nation's Report Card: America's high school graduates: Results from the 2005 NAEP High School Transcript Study*, by C. Shettle et al. (NCES 2007-467) (Washington, DC: Government Printing Office).

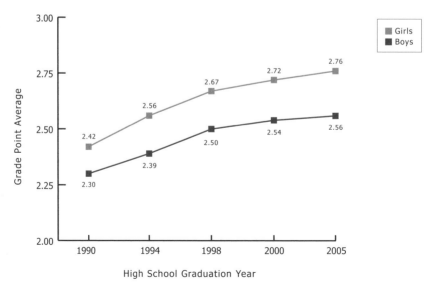

Figure 2. Grade Point Average in High School Mathematics and Science (Combined), by Gender, 1990–2005

Source: U.S. Department of Education, National Center for Education Statistics, 2007, *The Nation's Report Card: America's high school graduates: Results from the 2005 NAEP High School Transcript Study*, by C. Shettle et al. (NCES 2007-467) (Washington, DC: Government Printing Office).

On high-stakes math tests, however, boys continue to outscore girls, albeit by a small margin. A small gender gap persists on the mathematics section of the SAT and the ACT examinations (Halpern, Benbow, et al., 2007; AAUW, 2008). Fewer girls than boys take advanced placement (AP) exams in STEM-related subjects such as calculus, physics, computer science, and chemistry (see figure 3), and girls who take STEM AP exams earn lower scores than boys earn on average (see figure 4). Research on "stereotype threat," profiled in chapter 3, sheds light on the power of stereotypes to undermine girls' math test performance and may help explain the puzzle of girls' strong classroom performance and relatively weaker performance on high-stakes tests such as these.

One notable gain is girls' increased representation in the ranks of the highest achievers in mathematics. Among students with very high scores on math tests, boys continue to outnumber girls (Lubinski & Benbow, 1992, 2006; Hedges & Nowell, 1995); however, the proportion of girls among the highest math achievers has greatly increased during the past few decades. The Study of Mathematically Precocious Youth identifies seventh and eighth graders who score greater than 700 on the SAT math section (the top 0.01 percent or 1 in 10,000 students). Since the early 1980s the ratio of boys to girls in this extremely select group has dramatically declined from 13:1 (Benbow & Stanley, 1983) to around 3:1 in recent years (Brody & Mills, 2005; Halpern, Benbow, et al., 2007).

Students from historically disadvantaged groups such as African American and Hispanic students, both female and male, are less likely to have access to advanced courses in math and science in high school, which negatively affects their ability to enter and successfully complete STEM majors in college (May & Chubin, 2003; Frizell & Nave, 2008; Tyson et al., 2007; Perna et al., 2009). In 2005, 31 percent of Asian American and 16 percent of white high school graduates completed calculus, compared with 6 percent and 7 percent of African American and Hispanic high school graduates, respectively. Additionally, one-quarter of Asian American and one-tenth of white high school graduates took either the AP or International Baccalaureate exam in calculus, compared with just 3.2 percent of African American and 5.6 percent of Hispanic graduates (National Science Board, 2008). Yet even among underrepresented racial-ethnic groups, a growing number of girls are leaving high school well prepared in math and science and capable of pursuing STEM majors in college.

WOMEN IN STEM IN COLLEGES AND UNIVERSITIES

The transition between high school and college is a critical moment when many young women turn away from a STEM career path. Although women are the majority of college students, they are far less likely than their male peers to plan to major in a STEM field (see figure 5).

Figure 3. Students Taking Advanced Placement Tests in Mathematics and Science, by Gender, 2009

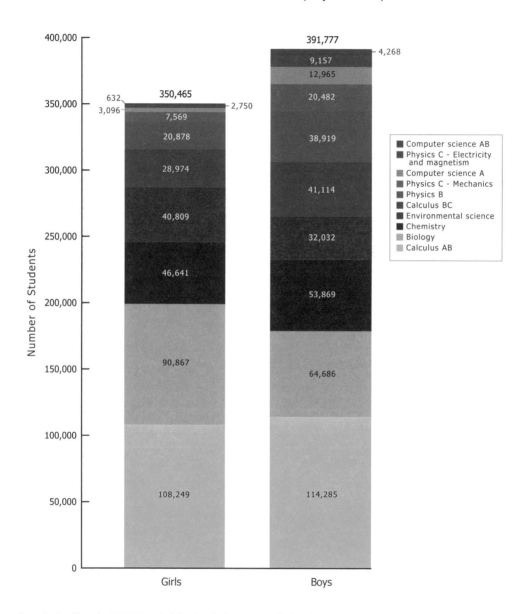

Source: Retrieved November 11, 2009, from the College Board website at www.collegeboard.com.

Figure 4. Average Scores on Advanced Placement Tests in Mathematics and Science Subjects, by Gender, 2009

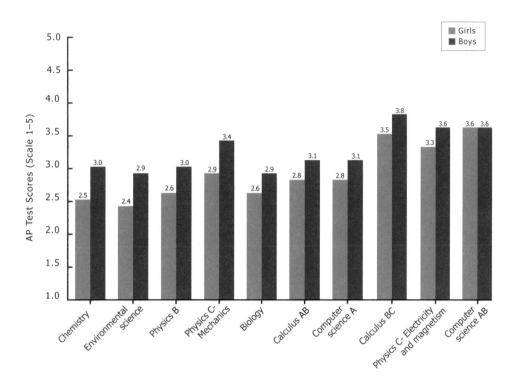

Source: Retrieved November 11, 2009, from the College Board website at www.collegeboard.com.

Almost one-third of all male freshmen (29 percent), compared with only 15 percent of all female freshmen, planned to major in a STEM field in 2006 (National Science Foundation, 2009b). The gender disparity in plans to major is even more significant when the biological sciences are not included. Just over one-fifth of male freshmen planned to major in engineering, computer science, or the physical sciences, compared with only about 5 percent of female freshmen (ibid.).

Women who enter STEM majors in college tend to be well qualified. Female and male first-year STEM majors are equally likely to have taken and earned high grades in the prerequisite math and science classes in high school and to have confidence in their math and science abilities (Brainard & Carlin, 1998; U.S. Department of Education, National Center for Education Statistics, 2000; Vogt et al., 2007). Nevertheless, many of these academically capable women

Figure 5. Intent of First-Year College Students to Major in STEM Fields, by Race-Ethnicity and Gender, 2006

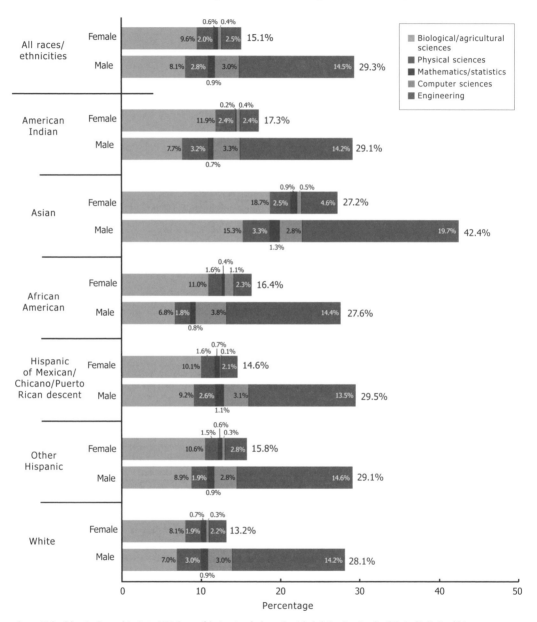

Source: Higher Education Research Institute, 2007, *Survey of the American freshman: Special tabulations* (Los Angeles, CA), cited in National Science Foundation, Division of Science Resources Statistics, 2009, *Women, minorities, and persons with disabilities in science and engineering: 2009* (NSF 09-305) (Arlington, VA), Table B-8.

leave STEM majors early in their college careers, as do many of their male peers (Seymour & Hewitt, 1997). For example, in engineering the national rate of retention from entry into the major to graduation is just under 60 percent for women and men (Ohland et al., 2008). Although the overall retention of female undergraduates in STEM is similar to the retention rate for men and has improved over time (U.S. Department of Education, National Center for Education Statistics, 2000; Xie & Shauman, 2003), understanding why women leave STEM majors is still an important area of research. Women make up a smaller number of STEM students from the start, so the loss of women from these majors is of special concern. Chapter 6 profiles the work of researchers Barbara Whitten, Jane Margolis, and Allan Fisher, showing the role of departmental culture in attracting and retaining female computer science and physics majors.

Despite the still relatively small percentages of women majoring in some STEM fields, the overall proportion of STEM bachelor's degrees awarded to women has increased dramatically during the past four decades, although women's representation varies by field.

In 2006, women earned the majority of bachelor's degrees in biology, one-half of bachelor's degrees in chemistry, and nearly one-half in math. Women earned a much smaller proportion

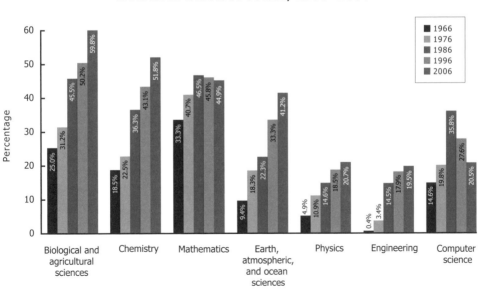

Figure 6. Bachelor's Degrees Earned by Women in Selected Fields, 1966–2006

Source: National Science Foundation, Division of Science Resources Statistics, 2008, *Science and engineering degrees: 1966–2006* (Detailed Statistical Tables) (NSF 08-321) (Arlington, VA), Table 11, Author's analysis of Tables 34, 35, 38, & 39.

Figure 7. Bachelor's Degrees Earned in Selected Science and Engineering Fields, by Gender, 2007

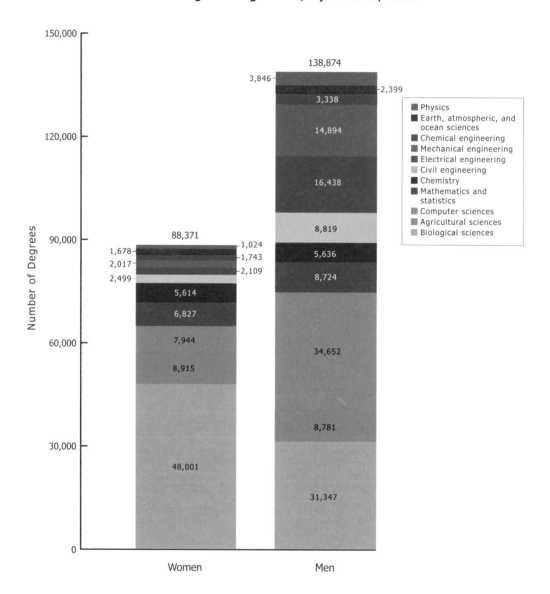

Source: National Science Foundation, Division of Science Resources Statistics, 2009, *Women, minorities, and persons with disabilities in science and engineering: 2009* (NSF 09-305) (Arlington, VA), Tables C-4 and C-5.

of bachelor's degrees awarded in physics, engineering, and computer science. In fact, as figure 6 shows, women's representation in computer science is actually declining—a stark reminder that women's progress cannot be taken for granted. In the mid-1980s women earned slightly more than one-third (36 percent) of the bachelor's degrees in computer science; by 2006 that number had dropped to 20 percent.

The size of the STEM disciplines, and, therefore, the number of degrees awarded, varies dramatically. As figure 7 shows, women earned 48,001 biological science degrees in 2007, compared with only 7,944 computer science degrees, 2,109 electrical engineering degrees, and 1,024 physics degrees. In comparison, men earned 31,347 biological science degrees, 34,652 computer science degrees, 16,438 electrical engineering degrees, and 3,846 physics degrees.

Figure 8. Bachelor's Degrees Earned by Underrepresented Racial-Ethnic Groups in Selected STEM Fields, by Gender, 2007

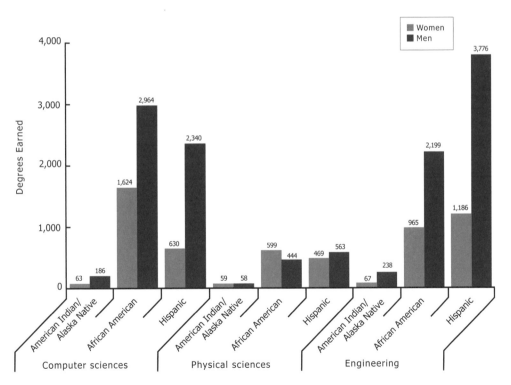

Note: Racial-ethnic groups include U.S. citizens and permanent residents only. Data based on degree-granting institutions eligible to participate in Title IV federal financial aid programs.
Source: National Science Foundation, Division of Science Resources Statistics, 2009, *Women, minorities, and persons with disabilities in science and engineering: 2009* (NSF 09-305) (Arlington, VA), Table C-14.

Trends in bachelor's degrees earned by women from underrepresented racial-ethnic groups (African American, Hispanic, and Native American/Alaskan Native) generally mirror the overall pattern; however, in some cases the gender gap in degrees earned by African American and Hispanic women and men is much smaller or even reversed (see figure 8). For example, African American women earned 57 percent of physical science degrees awarded to African Americans in 2007; still, the overall number of African American women earning physical science bachelor's degrees was less than 600.

Women's representation among doctoral degree recipients in STEM fields also has improved in the last 40 years (see figure 9). In 1966, women earned about one-eighth of the doctorates in the biological and agricultural sciences, 6 percent of the doctorates in chemistry and mathematics, and 3 percent or less of the doctorates in earth, atmospheric, and ocean sciences; physics; engineering; and computer science. Forty years later, in 2006, women earned almost one-half of the doctorates in the biological and agricultural sciences; around one-third of the doctorates in earth, atmospheric, and ocean sciences, chemistry, and math; and approximately one-fifth of the doctorates in computer science, engineering, and physics.

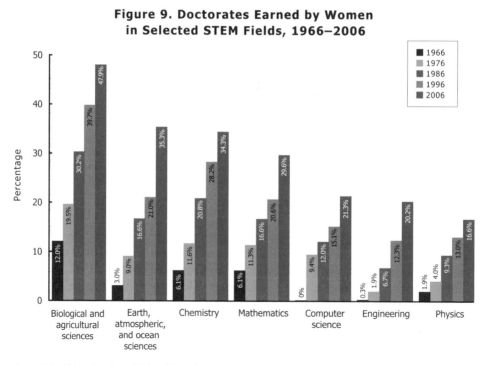

Figure 9. Doctorates Earned by Women in Selected STEM Fields, 1966–2006

Source: National Science Foundation, Division of Science Resources Statistics, 2008, *Science and engineering degrees: 1966–2006* (Detailed Statistical Tables) (NSF 08-321) (Arlington, VA), Table 25, Author's analysis of Tables 34, 35, 38, & 39.

Title IX and Gender Equity in STEM

Title IX of the Education Amendments of 1972 prohibits sex discrimination in education programs and activities that receive federal financial assistance. The law states, "No person in the United States shall, on the basis of sex, be excluded from participation in, be denied the benefits of, or be subjected to discrimination under any educational program or activity receiving federal financial assistance" (20 U.S. Code § 1681). Title IX covers nearly all colleges and universities. To ensure compliance with the law, Title IX regulations require institutions that receive any form of federal education funding to evaluate their current policies and practices and adopt and publish grievance procedures and a policy against sex discrimination.

When Congress enacted Title IX, the law was intended to help women achieve equal access to all aspects of education at all levels. During the last 37 years, however, Title IX has been applied mostly to sports. Recent efforts by Congress have brought attention to how Title IX could be used to improve the climate for and representation of women in STEM fields.

Critics argue that women do not face discrimination in STEM fields but rather that women are less interested than men in certain STEM fields and that enforcement of Title IX could lead to a quota system in the sciences (Tierney, 2008; Munro, 2009). Title IX requires neither quotas nor proportionality, and it cannot address gender gaps in participation due to personal choices; however, Title IX reviews can help identify institutional policies and practices that negatively, and in some cases inadvertently, affect personal choices in gender-specific ways (Pieronek, 2005). Simply put, Title IX can help create a climate where women and men of similar talent who want to be scientists or engineers have equal opportunity to do so.

A report by the U.S. Government Accountability Office (2004) focused on Title IX in STEM disciplines and concluded that federal agencies need to do more to ensure that colleges and universities receiving federal funds comply with Title IX. In response to these findings, federal agencies, including NASA and the Department of Energy in conjunction with the Department of Education and the Department of Justice, have begun to conduct Title IX compliance reviews more regularly (Pieronek, 2009).

In general the number of doctoral degrees in STEM disciplines earned by women from underrepresented racial-ethnic backgrounds also increased during the past four decades but still remains a small proportion of the total. For example, in 2007, African American women earned 2.2 percent of the doctorates awarded in the biological sciences and less than 2 percent of those awarded in engineering, computer sciences, the physical sciences, and mathematics and statistics. The proportions were similar for Hispanic women and even smaller for Native American women (National Science Foundation, 2009b). Although women have clearly made great progress in earning doctorates in STEM fields, at the doctoral level women remain underrepresented in every STEM field except biology.

WOMEN IN THE STEM WORKFORCE

Consistent with the increased representation of women among STEM degree recipients, women's representation in the STEM workforce has also improved significantly in recent decades; yet, as figure 10 shows, women are still underrepresented in many STEM professions.

In fields such as the biological sciences, women have had a sizeable presence as far back as 1960, when women made up about 27 percent of biologists. Forty years later, in 2000, women made up about 44 percent of the field. On the other end of the spectrum, women made up a mere 1 percent of engineers in 1960 and only about 11 percent of engineers by 2000 (see figure 11). This is an impressive increase, but women still make up only a small minority of working engineers. Overall, progress has been made, but women remain vastly outnumbered in many STEM fields, especially engineering and physics.

Figure 10. Women in Selected STEM Occupations, 2008

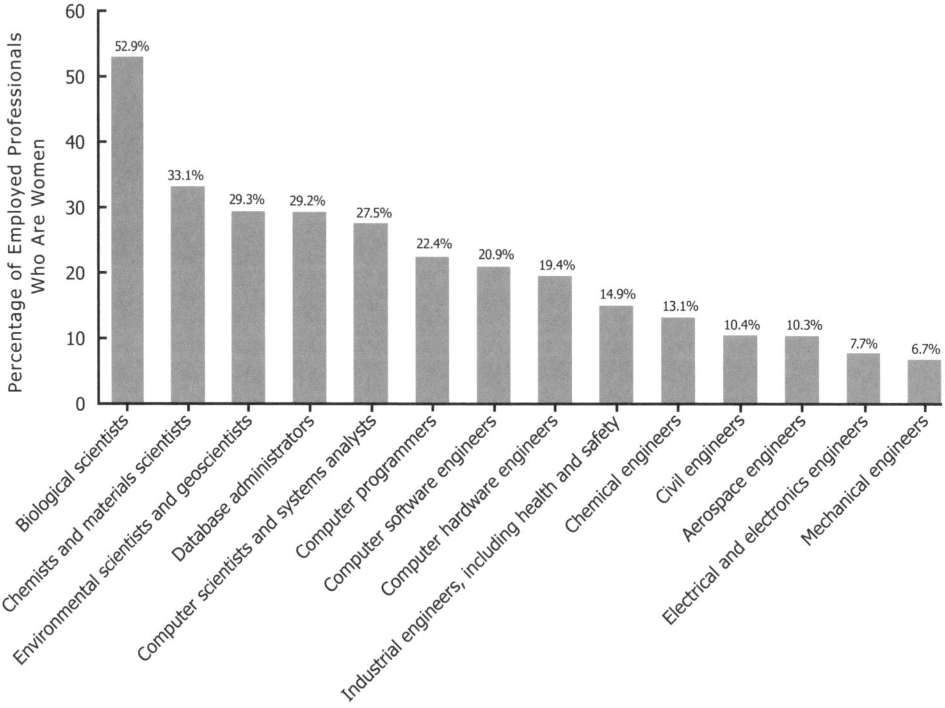

Note: Occupations are self-reported.
Source: U.S. Department of Labor, Bureau of Labor Statistics, 2009, *Women in the labor force: A databook* (Report 1018) (Washington, DC), Table 11.

Figure 11. Women in Selected STEM Occupations, 1960–2000

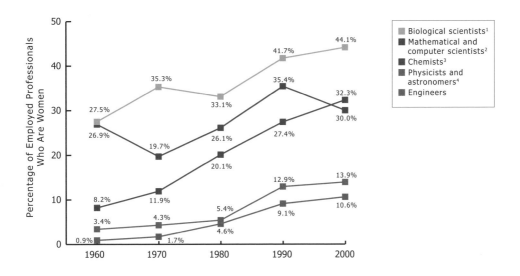

Notes: Data on postsecondary teachers by field of instruction were not gathered in the 2000 census, so postsecondary teachers are not included here. When postsecondary teachers were included from 1960 to 1990, the general trends remained the same.

[1] In the 1980 and 1990 censuses, data include life scientists as well as biological scientists.

[2] In the 1960 census, no category for computer scientists was included; in the 1970 census, the category was titled "mathematicians and computer specialists."

[3] In the 1980 and 1990 censuses, the category was titled "chemists except biochemists"; in the 2000 census, the category was titled "chemists and material scientists."

[4] In the 1960 census, the category was titled "physicists."

Source: U.S. Census Bureau, 1960, 1970, 1980, 1990, & 2000, Census of the population (Washington, DC).

Among workers who hold doctorates, men represent a clear majority in all STEM fields. Figures 12a and 12b show that men far outnumber women, even in the biological sciences.

In the academic workforce, women's representation varies by discipline as well as tenure status. Forty percent of the full-time faculty in degree-granting colleges and universities in the United States in 2005 were women; however, women's representation in STEM disciplines was significantly lower. Women made up less than one-quarter of the faculty in computer and information sciences (22 percent), math (19 percent), the physical sciences (18 percent), and engineering (12 percent). In the life sciences, an area in which many people assume that women have achieved parity, women made up only one-third (34 percent) of the faculty. In all cases women were better represented in lower faculty ranks than in higher ranks among STEM faculty in four-year colleges and universities (Di Fabio et al., 2008).

The situation is even more severe for women from underrepresented racial-ethnic backgrounds. Of the more than 7,000 computer-science doctoral faculty in 2006, only 60 were

Figure 12a. Workers with Doctorates in the Computer and Information Sciences Workforce, by Gender and Employment Status, 2006

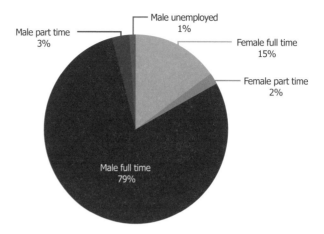

Note: The number of female unemployed workers was not available due to small sample size.

Source: National Science Foundation, Division of Science Resources Statistics, 2009, *Characteristics of doctoral scientists and engineers in the United States: 2006* (Detailed Statistical Tables) (NSF 09-317) (Arlington, VA), Authors' analysis of Table 2.

Figure 12b. Workers with Doctorates in the Biological, Agricultural, and Environmental Life Science Workforce, by Gender and Employment Status, 2006

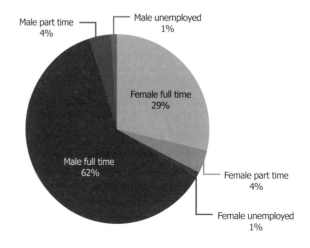

Note: The percentages do not equal 100 due to rounding.

Source: National Science Foundation, Division of Science Resources Statistics, 2009, *Characteristics of doctoral scientists and engineers in the United States: 2006* (Detailed Statistical Tables) (NSF 09-317) (Arlington, VA), Authors' analysis of Table 2.

African American women; numbers for Hispanic and Native American women were too low to report. African American women also made up less than 1 percent of the 17,150 postsecondary teachers in engineering. Even in the biological sciences the number of African American and Hispanic female faculty was low. Of the nearly 25,000 postsecondary teachers in the biological sciences, 380 were African American women and 300 were Hispanic women (ibid.).

Women's representation among tenured faculty is lower than one would expect based on the supply of female science and engineering doctoral degree recipients in recent decades (Kulis et al., 2002). The path from elementary school to a STEM career has often been compared to a pipeline. This metaphor suggests that as the number of girls who study STEM subjects in elementary, middle, and secondary school increases (more girls go into the pipeline), the number of women who become scientists and engineers will also increase (more women come out of the pipeline), and gender disparities in representation will disappear. This has not happened at the expected rate, especially at the tenured faculty level in science and engineering. If we compare the percentage of tenured female faculty in 2006 with the percentage of STEM doctorates awarded to women in 1996 (allowing 10 years for an individual to start an academic job and earn tenure), in most STEM fields the drop-off is pronounced. For example, women earned 12 percent of the doctorates in engineering in 1996 but were only 7 percent of the tenured faculty in engineering in 2006. Even in fields like biology, where women now receive about one-half of doctorates and received 42 percent in 1996, women made up less than one-quarter of tenured faculty and only 34 percent of tenure-track faculty in 2006 (National Science Foundation, 2008, 2009a). Women make up larger percentages of the lower-paying, nontenured STEM faculty positions (see figure 13).

Several studies have found a gender difference in hiring in STEM academic disciplines (Bentley & Adamson, 2003; Nelson & Rogers, n.d.; Ginther & Kahn, 2006). Although recent research found that when women do apply for STEM faculty positions at major research universities they are more likely than men to be hired, smaller percentages of qualified women apply for these positions in the first place (National Research Council, 2009). Improving women's position among STEM faculty will apparently require more than simply increasing the pool of female STEM degree holders (Valian, 1998; Kulis et al., 2002).

Cathy Trower and her colleagues at the Collaborative on Academic Careers in Higher Education (COACHE) at Harvard University found that female STEM faculty express lower job satisfaction than do their male peers. Lower satisfaction leads to higher turnover and a loss of talent in science and engineering. Trower's research, profiled in chapter 7, suggests that the climate of science and engineering departments is closely related to satisfaction of female faculty and that providing effective mentoring and work-life policies can help improve job satisfaction and, hence, the retention of female STEM faculty.

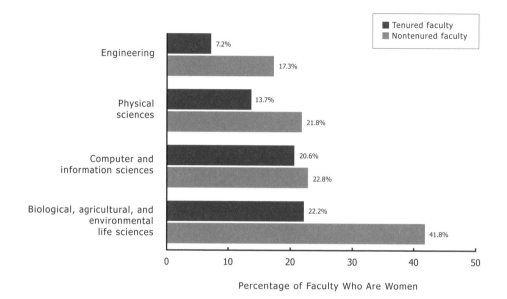

Figure 13. Female STEM Faculty in Four-Year Educational Institutions, by Discipline and Tenure Status, 2006

Legend:
- ■ Tenured faculty
- ■ Nontenured faculty

Engineering:
- 7.2%
- 17.3%

Physical sciences:
- 13.7%
- 21.8%

Computer and information sciences:
- 20.6%
- 22.8%

Biological, agricultural, and environmental life sciences:
- 22.2%
- 41.8%

Percentage of Faculty Who Are Women

Source: National Science Foundation, Division of Science Resources Statistics, 2009, *Characteristics of doctoral scientists and engineers in the United States: 2006* (Detailed Statistical Tables) (NSF 09-317) (Arlington, VA), Author's analysis of Table 20.

Women working in STEM fields tend to have higher earnings than do other women in the workforce, although a gender pay gap exists in STEM occupations as in other fields. For example, in 2009 the average starting salary for bachelor's degree recipients in marketing was just over $42,000 a year, and bachelor's degree recipients in accounting received starting salaries averaging around $48,500 a year. In comparison, starting salaries for bachelor's degree holders in computer science averaged around $61,500, and average starting salaries were just under $66,000 for individuals holding bachelor's degrees in chemical engineering (National Association of Colleges and Employers, 2009). As these numbers indicate, many STEM careers can provide women increased earning potential and greater economic security.

Recent studies of scientists, engineers, and technologists in business and the high-tech industry have found that women in these fields have higher attrition rates than do both their male peers and women in other occupations (Hewlett et al., 2008; Simard et al., 2008). The studies highlight midcareer as a critical time for these women. Hewlett et al. (2008) at the Center for Work-Life Policy at Harvard University found that female scientists, engineers, and technologists are fairly well represented at the lower rungs on corporate ladders

(41 percent). More than half (52 percent), however, quit their jobs by midcareer (about 10 years into their careers). High-tech companies in particular lost 41 percent of their female employees, compared with only 17 percent of their male employees. In engineering, women have higher attrition rates than their male peers have, despite similar levels of stated satisfaction and education. The Society of Women Engineers (2006) conducted a retention study of more than 6,000 individuals who earned an engineering degree between 1985 and 2003. One-quarter of female engineers surveyed were either not employed at all or not employed in engineering or a related field, while only one-tenth of men surveyed had left the engineering field.

WHY SO FEW?

Academic research on this topic is prolific, with three themes emerging from the literature. First, the notion that men are mathematically superior and innately better suited to STEM fields than women are remains a common belief, with a large number of articles addressing cognitive gender differences as an explanation for the small numbers of women in STEM. A second theme revolves around girls' lack of interest in STEM. A third theme involves the STEM workplace, with issues ranging from work-life balance to bias. The remainder of this chapter summarizes and examines these themes and concludes with an introduction to the research projects profiled in chapters 2 through 9.

Cognitive Sex Differences

As noted earlier, a difference in average math performance between girls and boys no longer exists in the general school population (Hyde et al., 2008). Nevertheless, the issue of cognitive sex differences, including mathematical ability, remains hotly contested. Lynn and Irwing (2004) found small or no differences in average IQ between the sexes; that is, neither girls nor boys are the "smarter sex."[2] Other researchers have found, however, that girls and boys tend to have different cognitive strengths and weaknesses. Generally, boys perform better on tasks using spatial orientation and visualization and on certain quantitative tasks that

Methodology

Using multiple databases, including Web of Science, ProQuest, Social Science Citation Index, and J-Stor, AAUW reviewed hundreds of academic articles written during the past 25 years on the topic of women in science and engineering. Articles from the fields of psychology, sociology, education, economics, neuroscience, and endocrinology were examined. The literature review informed this chapter, and it was used to help identify the eight research findings profiled in chapters 2 through 9. These projects were chosen because they each address an important issue with the potential to influence public understanding. The profiled findings are well respected in the research community, as measured by publication in peer-reviewed journals, number of citations, and other forms of public recognition. These projects were conducted within the past 15 years.

---

[2]Some research suggests that women and men achieve similar IQ results using different parts of the brain (Haier et al., 2005).

rely on those skills. Girls outperform boys on tests relying on verbal skills, especially writing, as well as some tests involving memory and perceptual speed (Hedges & Nowell, 1995; Kimura, 2002; Halpern, Aronson, et al., 2007).

One of the largest gender gaps in cognitive skills is seen in the area of spatial skills and specifically on measures of mental rotation, with boys consistently outscoring girls (Linn & Petersen, 1985; Voyer et al., 1995). Many people consider spatial skills to be important for success in fields like engineering, although the connection between spatial abilities and success in STEM careers is not definitive (Ceci et al., 2009). Whether or not well-developed spatial skills are necessary for success in science and engineering, research shows that spatial skills can be improved fairly easily with training (Baenninger & Newcombe, 1989; Vasta et al., 1996). Among the most promising research findings in this field are those of Sheryl Sorby, whose work is profiled in chapter 5. Sorby and Baartmans (2000) and their colleagues designed and implemented a successful course to improve the spatial-visualization skills of first-year engineering students who had poorly developed spatial skills. More than three-quarters of female engineering students who took the course remained in the school of engineering, compared with about one-half of the female students who did not take the course. Poor or underdeveloped spatial skills may deter girls from pursuing math or science courses or careers, but these skills can be improved fairly easily.

Biology is not destiny

Ceci et al. (2009) reviewed more than 400 articles exploring the causes of women's underrepresentation in STEM fields, including biological as well as social factors, and concluded that the research on sex differences in brain structure and hormones is inconclusive. Female and male brains are indeed physically distinct, but how these differences translate into specific cognitive strengths and weaknesses remains unclear. Likewise, evidence for cognitive sex differences based on hormonal exposure is mixed. Ceci et al. found that hormonal exposure, especially in gestation, does have a role in cognitive sex differences. Overall, however, the researchers concluded, "Evidence for a hormonal basis of the dearth of female scientists" is "weaker than the evidence for other factors," such as gender differences in preferences and sociocultural influences on girls' performance on gatekeeper tests (p. 224).

Differences in the representation of women in science and math fields cross-culturally and over time also support the role of sociocultural factors for explaining gender gaps in these fields (Andreescu et al., 2008). As discussed earlier, the ratio of boys to girls among children identified as mathematically precocious has decreased dramatically in the last 30 years, far faster than it would take a genetic change to travel through the population. Also, while in the vast majority of countries more boys than girls scored above the 99th percentile in mathematics on the 2003 Program for International Student Assessment, in Iceland and Thailand more girls than boys scored above the 99th percentile (Guiso et al., 2008). Differences between countries and over time illustrate the importance of culture in the development of mathematical skills.

Scientists and engineers are not necessarily the highest math achievers

Boys outnumber girls at the very high end of the math test score distribution. Some researchers have suggested that this gender difference accounts for the small number of women in certain STEM fields. This logic has two main flaws. First, as mentioned above, girls have made rapid inroads into the ranks of children identified as "mathematically gifted" in the past 30 years, while women's representation in mathematically demanding fields such as physics, computer science, and engineering has grown slowly. That is, fewer women pursue STEM careers than would be expected based on the number of girls who earn very high math scores. Second, Weinberger (2005) found that the science and engineering workforce is not populated primarily by the highest-scoring math students, male or female. Less than one-third of college-educated white men in the engineering, math, computer science, and physical science workforce scored higher than 650 on the SAT math exam, and more than one-third had SAT math scores below 550—the math score of the average humanities major. Even though a correlation exists between high school math test scores and later entry into STEM education and careers, very high math scores are not necessarily a prerequisite for success in STEM fields.

"Just Not Interested"

Many girls and women report that they are not interested in science and engineering. In a 2009 poll of young people ages 8–17 by the American Society for Quality, 24 percent of boys but only 5 percent of girls said they were interested in an engineering career. Another recent poll found that 74 percent of college-bound boys ages 13–17 said that computer science or computing would be a good college major for them compared with 32 percent of their female peers (WGBH Education Foundation & Association for Computing Machinery, 2009). From early adolescence, girls express less interest in math or science careers than boys do (Lapan et al., 2000; Turner et al., 2008). Even girls and women who excel in mathematics often do not pursue STEM fields. In studies of high mathematics achievers, for example, women are more likely to secure degrees in the humanities, life sciences, and social sciences than in math, computer science, engineering, or the physical sciences; the reverse is true for men (Lubinski & Benbow, 2006).

Interest in an occupation is influenced by many factors, including a belief that one can succeed in that occupation (Eccles [Parsons] et al., 1983; Correll, 2004; Eccles, 2006). The work of

Shelley Correll, profiled in chapter 4, shows that girls assess their mathematical ability lower than do boys with equivalent past mathematical achievement. At the same time, girls hold themselves to a higher standard in subjects like math, where boys are considered to excel. Because of this, girls are less likely to believe that they will succeed in a STEM field and, therefore, are less likely to express interest in a STEM career.

Pajares (2005) found that gender differences in self-confidence in STEM subjects begin in middle school and increase in high school and college, with girls reporting less confidence than boys do in their math and science ability. In part, boys develop greater confidence in STEM through experience developing relevant skills. A number of studies have shown that gender differences in self-confidence disappear when variables such as previous achievement or opportunity to learn are controlled (Lent et al., 1986; Zimmerman & Martinez-Pons, 1990; Cooper & Robinson, 1991; Pajares, 1996, 2005). Students who lack confidence in their math or science skills are less likely to engage in tasks that require those skills and will more quickly give up in the face of difficulty. Girls and women may be especially vulnerable to losing confidence in STEM areas. The research of Carol Dweck, profiled in chapter 2, has implications for improving self-confidence. Dweck's research shows that when a girl believes that she can become smarter and learn what she needs to know in STEM subjects—as opposed to believing that a person is either born with science and math ability or not—she is more likely to succeed in a STEM field.

A belief that one can succeed in a STEM field is important but is not the only factor in establishing interest in a STEM career. Culturally prescribed gender roles also influence occupational interest (Low et al., 2005). A review of child vocational development by Hartung et al. (2005) found that children—and girls especially—develop beliefs that they cannot pursue particular occupations because they perceive them as inappropriate for their gender.

Jacquelynne Eccles, a leading researcher in the field of occupational choice, has spent the past 30 years developing a model and collecting evidence about career choice. Her work suggests that occupational choice is influenced by a person's values as well as expectancy for success (Eccles [Parsons] et al., 1983; Eccles, 1994, 2006). Well-documented gender differences exist in the value that women and men place on doing work that contributes to society, with women more likely than men to prefer work with a clear social purpose (Jozefowicz et al., 1993; Konrad et al., 2000; Margolis et al., 2002; Lubinski & Benbow, 2006; Eccles, 2006). The source of this gender difference is a subject of debate: Some claim that the difference is innate, while others claim that it is a result of gender socialization. Regardless of the origin of the difference, most people do not view STEM occupations as directly benefiting society or individuals (National Academy of Engineering, 2008; Diekman et al., 2009). As a result, STEM careers often do not appeal to women (or men) who value making a social contribution

(Eccles, 1994; Sax, 1994). Certain STEM subdisciplines with a clearer social purpose, such as biomedical engineering and environmental engineering, have succeeded in attracting higher percentages of women than have other subdisciplines like mechanical or electrical engineering (Gibbons, 2009).

Despite girls' lower stated interest in science and engineering compared with boys, recent research suggests that there are ways to increase girls' interest in STEM areas (Turner & Lapan, 2005; Eisenhart, 2008; Plant et al., 2009). Plant et al. (2009) reported an increase in middle school girls' interest in engineering after the girls were exposed to a 20-minute narrative delivered by a computer-generated female agent describing the lives of female engineers and the benefits of engineering careers. The narrative included positive statements about students' abilities to meet the demands of engineering careers and counteracted stereotypes of engineering as an antisocial, unusual career for women while emphasizing the people-oriented and socially beneficial aspects of engineering. Another ongoing study and outreach project is focusing on educating high-achieving, mostly minority, high school girls about what scientists and engineers actually do and how they contribute to society. Although the girls knew almost nothing about engineering at the start of the study, of the 66 percent of girls still participating after two years, 80 percent were seriously considering a career in engineering (Eisenhart, 2008). The Engineer Your Life website (www.engineeryourlife.com), a project of the WGBH Educational Foundation and the National Academy of Engineering, has also been shown to increase high school girls' interest in pursuing engineering as a career. In a survey by Paulsen and Bransfield (2009), 88 percent of 631 girls said that the website made them more interested in engineering as a career, and 76 percent said that it inspired them to take an engineering course in college. Although these studies generally relied on small samples and in a number of cases no long-term follow-up has been done with participants, the results are promising.

Research on interest in science and engineering does not usually consider gender, race, and ethnicity simultaneously. Of course, gender and race do interact to create different cultural roles and expectations for women (and men) from different racial-ethnic backgrounds. Assumptions about the mismatch between women's interests and STEM often are based on the experiences of white women. In the African American community, for example, many of the characteristics that are considered appropriate for African American women, such as high self-esteem, independence, and assertiveness, can lead to success in STEM fields (Hanson, 2004). Young African American women express more interest in STEM fields than do young white women (Hanson, 2004; Fouad & Walker, 2005). The number of African American women in STEM remains low, however, suggesting that other barriers are important for this community (ibid.).

Workplace Environment, Bias, and Family Responsibilities

As mentioned above, women leave STEM fields at a higher rate than do their male peers (Society of Women Engineers, 2006; Hewlett et al., 2008; Frehill et al., 2009). Workplace environment, bias, and family responsibilities all play a role.

Workplace environment

In the study of STEM professionals in the private sector described earlier, Hewlett et al. (2008) found that many women appear to encounter a series of challenges at midcareer that contribute to their leaving careers in STEM industries. Women cited feelings of isolation, an unsupportive work environment, extreme work schedules, and unclear rules about advancement and success as major factors in their decision to leave. Although women and men in industry and business leave STEM careers at significantly different rates, the situation in academia is somewhat more nuanced. In a recent study on attrition among STEM faculty, Xu (2008) showed that female and male faculty leave at similar rates; however, women are more likely than men to consider changing jobs within academia. Women's higher turnover intention in academia (which is the best predictor of actual turnover) is mainly due to dissatisfaction with departmental culture, advancement opportunities, faculty leadership, and research support. Goulden et al. (2009) compared men and women in the sciences who are married with children and found that the women were 35 percent less likely to enter a tenure-track position after receiving a doctorate.

Bias

Women in STEM fields can experience bias that negatively influences their progress and participation. Although instances of explicit bias may be decreasing, implicit bias continues to have an adverse effect. Implicit biases may reflect, be stronger than, or in some cases contradict explicitly held beliefs or values. Therefore, even individuals who espouse a belief of gender equity and equality may harbor implicit biases about gender and, hence, negative gender stereotypes about women and girls in science and math (Valian, 1998). Nosek et al. (2002a) found that majorities of both women and men of all racial-ethnic groups hold a strong implicit association of male with science and female with liberal arts. This research is profiled in chapter 8.

Research has also pointed to bias in peer review (Wenneras & Wold, 1997) and hiring (Steinpreis et al., 1999; Trix & Psenka, 2003). For example, Wenneras and Wold found that a female postdoctoral applicant had to be significantly more productive than a male applicant to receive the same peer review score. This meant that she either had to publish at least three more papers in a prestigious science journal or an additional 20 papers in lesser-known specialty journals to be judged as productive as a male applicant. The authors concluded that the systematic underrating of female applicants could help explain the lower success rate of female scientists in achieving high academic rank compared with their male counterparts.

Trix and Psenka (2003) found systematic differences in letters of recommendation for academic faculty positions for female and male applicants. The researchers concluded that recommenders (the majority of whom were men) rely on accepted gender schema in which, for example, women are not expected to have significant accomplishments in a field like academic medicine. Letters written for women are more likely to refer to their compassion, teaching, and effort as opposed to their achievements, research, and ability, which are the characteristics highlighted for male applicants. While nothing is wrong with being compassionate, trying hard, and being a good teacher, arguably these traits are less valued than achievements, research, and ability for success in academic medicine. The authors concluded, "Recommenders unknowingly used selective categorization and perception, also known as stereotyping, in choosing what features to include in their profiles of the female applicants" (p. 215).

Research profiled in chapter 9 shows that when women are acknowledged as successful in arenas that are considered male in character, women are less well liked and more personally derogated than are equivalently successful men. Being disliked can affect career outcomes, leading to lower evaluations and less access to organizational rewards. These results suggest that gender stereotypes can prompt bias in evaluative judgments of women in male-dominated environments, even when these women have proved themselves to be successful and demonstrated their competence (Heilman et al., 2004).

Biases do change. Today the fields viewed as stereotypically male have narrowed considerably compared with even 30 years ago. Life and health sciences are seen as more appropriate for women, while the physical or hard sciences and engineering fields are still considered masculine domains (Farenga & Joyce, 1999).

Family responsibilities

Many people think that women leave STEM academic careers because they cannot balance work and family responsibilities (Mason et al., 2009; Xie & Shauman, 2003); however, research evidence by Xu (2008) points to a more nuanced relationship between family responsibilities and academic STEM careers. Research shows that being single is a good predictor that a woman will be hired for a tenure-track job and promoted. Research also shows, however, that marriage is a good predictor for both women and men of being hired as an assistant professor (Xie & Shauman, 2003; Ginther & Kahn, 2006). Married women in STEM appear to have a disadvantage compared with married men in relation to tenure and promotion decisions only if the married women have children (Xie & Shauman, 2003).

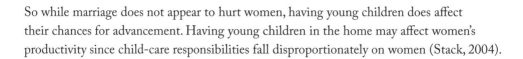

So while marriage does not appear to hurt women, having young children does affect their chances for advancement. Having young children in the home may affect women's productivity since child-care responsibilities fall disproportionately on women (Stack, 2004).

Some telling statistics point to the difficulties that mothers still face in an academic environment. Mason and Goulden (2002) found that among tenured faculty in the sciences 12 to 14 years after earning a doctorate, 70 percent of the men but only 50 percent of the women had children living in their home. The same study found that among science professors who had babies within the first five years after receiving a doctorate, 77 percent of the men but only 53 percent of the women had achieved tenure 12 to 14 years after earning a doctorate. These disparities were not unique to, and not always worse in, STEM fields. In another Mason and Goulden study (2004), more than twice as many female academics (38 percent) as male academics (18 percent) indicated that they had fewer children than they had wanted.

In business and industry both women and men identify family responsibilities as a possible barrier to advancement, but women are affected differently than men by this "family penalty" (Simard et al., 2008, p. 5). Although both women and men feel that having a family hinders their success at work, women are more likely than men to report foregoing marriage or children and delaying having children. Among women and men with families, women are more likely to report that they are the primary caregiver and have a partner who also works full time. A recent retention study found that most women and men who left engineering said that interest in another career was a reason, but women were far more likely than men to also cite time and family-related issues (Society of Women Engineers, 2006; Frehill et al., 2008). Additionally, women in STEM are more likely to have a partner who is also in STEM and faces a similarly demanding work schedule. In a situation where a "two body problem" exists, the man's career is often given priority (Hewlett et al., 2008).

WHERE DO WE GO FROM HERE?

Multiple factors contribute to the underrepresentation of women and girls in STEM and, therefore, multiple solutions are needed to correct the imbalance. The remainder of this report profiles eight research findings, each of which offers practical ideas for helping girls and women reach their potential in science, technology, engineering, and mathematics. Selected for their relevance to public debate and their scientific credibility, these case studies provide important insights into the question of why so few women study and work in many STEM fields.

These findings provide evidence on the nurture side of the nature-nurture debate, demonstrating that social and environmental factors clearly contribute to the underrepresentation of women in science and engineering. The findings are organized into three areas: social and environmental factors that shape girls' achievements and interest in math and science; the college environment; and the continuing importance of bias, often operating at an unconscious level, as an obstacle to women's success in STEM fields.

Girls' Achievements and Interest in Math and Science Are Shaped by the Environment around Them

This report profiles four research projects that demonstrate the effects of societal beliefs and the learning environment on girls' achievements and interest in science and math. Chapter 2 profiles research showing that when teachers and parents tell girls that their intelligence can expand with experience and learning, girls do better on math tests and are more likely to want to continue to study math.

Chapter 3 examines research showing that negative stereotypes about girls' abilities in math are still relevant today and can lower girls' test performance and aspirations for science and engineering careers. When test administrators tell students that girls and boys are equally capable in math, the difference in performance disappears, illustrating the importance of the learning environment for encouraging girls' achievement and interest in math.

Chapter 4 profiles research on self-assessment, or how we view our own abilities. This research finds that girls assess their mathematical abilities lower than do boys with similar past mathematical achievements. At the same time, girls hold themselves to a higher standard than boys do in subjects like math, believing that they have to be exceptional to succeed in "male" fields. One result of girls' lower self-assessment of their math ability—even in the face of good grades and test scores—and their higher standard for performance is that fewer girls than boys aspire to STEM careers.

One of the most consistent, and largest, gender differences in cognitive abilities is found in the area of spatial skills, with boys and men consistently outperforming girls and women. Chapter 5 highlights research documenting that individuals' spatial skills consistently improve dramatically in a short time with a simple training course. If girls are in an environment that enhances their success in science and math with spatial skills training, they are more likely to develop their skills as well as their confidence and consider a future in a STEM field.

At Colleges and Universities, Little Changes Can Make a Big Difference in Attracting and Retaining Women in STEM

As described earlier, many girls graduate from high school well prepared to pursue a STEM career, but few of them major in science or engineering in college. Research profiled in chapter 6 demonstrates how small improvements in the culture of computer science and physics departments, such as changing admissions requirements, presenting a broader overview of the field in introductory courses, and providing a student lounge, can add up to big gains in female student recruitment and retention.

Likewise, colleges and universities can attract more female science and engineering faculty if they improve the integration of female faculty into the departmental culture. Research profiled in chapter 7 provides evidence that women are less satisfied with the academic workplace and more likely to leave it earlier in their careers than their male counterparts are. College and university administrators can recruit and retain more women by implementing mentoring programs and effective work-life policies for all faculty members.

Bias, Often Unconscious, Limits Women's Progress in Scientific and Engineering Fields

Research profiled in chapter 8 shows that most people continue to associate science and math fields with "male" and humanities and arts fields with "female," including individuals who actively reject these stereotypes. Implicit bias may influence girls' likelihood of identifying with and participating in math and science and also contributes to bias in education and the workplace—even among people who support gender equity. Taking the implicit bias test at https://implicit.harvard.edu can help people identify and understand their own implicit biases so that they can work to compensate for them.

Research profiled in chapter 9 shows that people not only associate math and science with "male" but also often hold negative opinions of women in "masculine" positions, like scientists or engineers. This research shows that people judge women to be less competent than men in "male" jobs unless women are clearly successful in their work. When a woman is clearly competent in a "masculine" job, she is considered to be less likable. Because both likability and competence are needed for success in the workplace, women in STEM fields can find themselves in a double bind.

Women have made impressive gains in science and engineering but are still a distinct minority in many science and engineering fields. The following eight research findings, taken together, suggest that creating environments that support girls' and women's achievements and interest in science and engineering will encourage more girls and women to pursue careers in these vital fields.

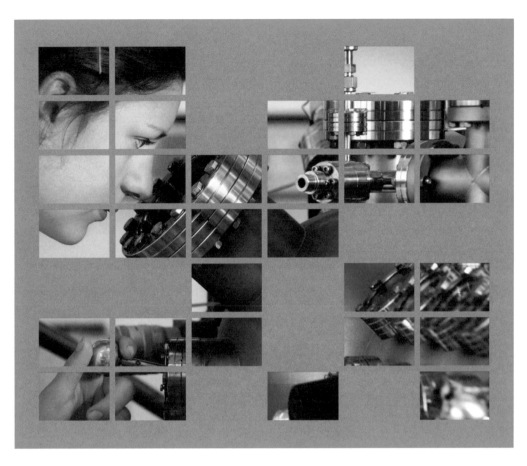

Chapter 2.
Beliefs about Intelligence

> So often, when something comes quickly to a student, we say, "Oh, you're really good at this." The message there is, "I think you're smart when you do something that doesn't require any effort or you haven't challenged yourself." Someone said to me recently, "In your culture, struggle is a bad word," and I thought … "That's right." We talk about it as an unfortunate thing, but when you think about a career in science or math or anything, of course you struggle. That's the name of the game! If you're going to discover something new or invent something new, it's a struggle. So I encourage educators to celebrate that, to say:
> "Who had a fantastic struggle? Tell me about your struggle!"
>
> —Carol Dweck[3]

Carol Dweck is a social and developmental psychologist at Stanford University. For 40 years she has studied the foundations of motivation. In an interview with AAUW, Dweck described how she first became interested in this topic:

> Since graduate school, I've been interested in how students cope with difficulty. Over the years it led me to understand that there were these whole frameworks that students brought to their achievement—that in one case made difficulty a terrible indictment but in the other case made difficulty a more exciting challenge. In one of my very first studies where I was giving failure problems, this little boy rubbed his hands together, smacked his lips, and said, "I love a challenge." And I thought, "Where is this kid from? Is he from another planet?" Either you cope with failure or you don't cope with failure, but to love it? That was something that was beyond my understanding, and I thought, "I'm going to figure out what this kid knows, and I'm going to bottle it." Over time I came to understand a framework in which you could relish something that someone else was considering a failure.

Dweck's research provides evidence that a "growth mindset" (viewing intelligence as a changeable, malleable attribute that can be developed through effort) as opposed to a "fixed mindset" (viewing intelligence as an inborn, uncontrollable trait) is likely to lead to greater persistence in the face of adversity and ultimately success in any realm (Dweck & Leggett, 1988; Blackwell et al., 2007; Dweck, 2006, 2008).

According to Dweck's research findings, individuals with a fixed mindset are susceptible to a loss of confidence when they encounter challenges, because they believe that if they are truly "smart," things will come easily to them. If they have to work hard at something, they tend to

---

[3]Carol S. Dweck is the Lewis and Virginia Eaton Professor of Psychology at Stanford University and a leading researcher in the field of student motivation. Her research focuses on theories of intelligence and highlights the critical role of mindsets in students' achievement. She has held professorships at Columbia and Harvard Universities. Her recent book, *Mindset* (Random House, 2006), has been widely acclaimed and is being translated into 17 languages.

question their abilities and lose confidence, and they are likely to give up because they believe they are "not good" at the task and, because their intelligence is fixed, will never be good at it. Individuals with a growth mindset, on the other hand, show a far greater belief in the power of effort, and in the face of difficulty, their confidence actually grows because they believe they are learning and getting smarter as a result of challenging themselves (see figure 14). Dweck and her colleagues found that students—in both middle school and college—are about equally divided between the two mindsets.

The significance of an individual's mindset often does not emerge until she or he faces challenges. In a supportive environment such as elementary school, students with a belief in fixed intelligence may do just fine; however, upon encountering the challenges of middle school, differences are likely to emerge between students with a fixed mindset about intelligence and those who believe that intelligence can increase with effort.

Because of this, and because math skills are particularly likely to be viewed as fixed (Williams & King, 1980), Dweck and her colleagues chose to test their theory by assessing the mindset of students entering junior high school and then tracking the students' math grades for two years. The study included 373 moderately high-achieving seventh graders in four successive entering classes of 67 to 114 students in a New York City public school. One math teacher taught each grade, and the school had no mathematics tracking. The researchers assessed whether each student held a fixed mindset or a growth mindset at the beginning of the study by asking the students to rank their agreement with a number of statements, such as, "You have a certain amount of intelligence, and you really can't do much to change it" and "You can learn new things, but you can't really change your basic intelligence." Nearly two years later, students who endorsed a strong growth mindset were outperforming those who held a fixed mindset, controlling for prior achievement. The researchers concluded that a student's motivational framework rather than her or his initial achievement determined whether students' math grades would improve.

In light of this finding the researchers conducted a second study to see if an intervention to teach seventh graders that intelligence is malleable would have any effect on their motivation in the classroom or on their grades. This study included 91 relatively low-achieving seventh graders from a different New York City public school. The students were split into two groups for a 25-minute period once each week for eight weeks. During this time, one-half of the students were taught that intelligence is malleable, and one-half were taught study skills. The students in the intervention group were taught that learning changes the brain and they should think of the brain as a muscle that becomes stronger, developing new connections and strengthening existing ones as someone learns. As a result, the person becomes smarter. The lessons also stressed that mistakes made in the course of learning are necessary and help

Figure 14. A Fixed versus a Growth Mindset

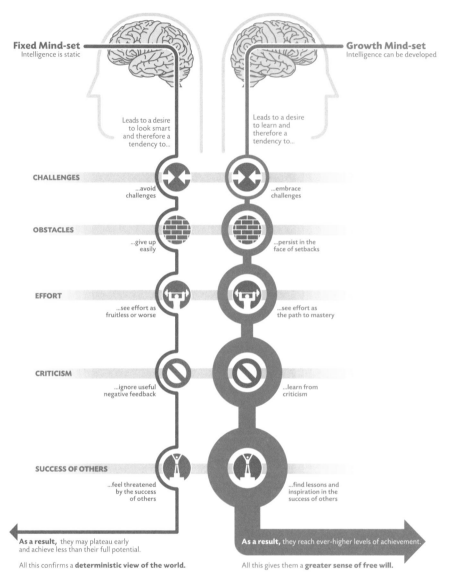

Fixed Mind-set
Intelligence is static

Growth Mind-set
Intelligence can be developed

Leads to a desire
to look smart
and therefore a
tendency to...

Leads to a desire
to learn and
therefore a
tendency to...

CHALLENGES

...avoid
challenges

...embrace
challenges

OBSTACLES

...give up
easily

...persist in the
face of setbacks

EFFORT

...see effort as
fruitless or worse

...see effort as
the path to mastery

CRITICISM

...ignore useful
negative feedback

...learn from
criticism

SUCCESS OF OTHERS

...feel threatened
by the success
of others

...find lessons and
inspiration in the
success of others

As a result, they may plateau early
and achieve less than their full potential.

All this confirms a **deterministic view of the world.**

As a result, they reach ever-higher levels of achievement.

All this gives them a **greater sense of free will.**

GRAPHIC BY NIGEL HOLMES

Source: Used with permission of Carol S. Dweck.

students learn. The lessons concluded with the message that students are in charge of this process and that being smart is a choice.

The results of this intervention were remarkable. While grades for all students in the experiment were declining on average before the intervention (between spring of sixth grade and fall of seventh grade), as is common in the transition to junior high school, for those students who were taught that intelligence is malleable, the decline in grades was reversed and their average math grades improved within a few months of the intervention. In contrast, the students in the control group continued to experience a decline in grades. This study provides evidence that the learning environment can influence an individual's mindset (fixed or growth).

Dweck's research is particularly relevant to women in STEM, because she and her colleagues have found that for both middle school and college students, a growth mindset protects girls and women from the influence of the stereotype that girls are not as good as boys at math (Good et al., 2003, 2009). If a girl with a fixed mindset encounters a challenging task or experiences a setback in math, she is more likely to believe the stereotype that girls are not as good as boys in math. On the other hand, if a girl believes that doing math is a skill that can be improved with practice, she thinks, in the words of Dweck, "OK, maybe girls haven't done well historically, maybe we weren't encouraged, maybe we didn't believe in ourselves, but these are acquirable skills." In the face of difficulty, girls with a growth mindset are more likely than girls with a fixed mindset to maintain their confidence and not succumb to stereotypes. A growth mindset, therefore, can be particularly useful to girls in STEM areas because it frees them of the ideas that their individual mathematical ability is fixed and that their ability is lower than that of boys by virtue of their gender. Interestingly, in cultures that produce a large number of math and science graduates, especially women, including South and East Asian cultures, the basis of success is generally attributed less to inherent ability and more to effort (Stevenson & Stigler, 1992).

A GROWTH MINDSET PROMOTES ACHIEVEMENT IN STEM

Dweck and others have also found gender gaps favoring boys in math and science performance among junior high and college students with fixed mindsets, while finding no gender gaps among their peers who have a growth mindset (Good et al., 2003; Grant & Dweck, 2003; Dweck, 2006). Dweck and her colleagues conducted a study in 2005 in which one group of adolescents was taught that great math thinkers had a lot of innate ability and natural talent (a fixed-mindset message), while another group was taught that great math thinkers were profoundly interested in and committed to math and worked hard to make their contributions (a growth-mindset message). On a subsequent challenging math test that the students were told gauged their mathematical ability, the girls who had received the fixed-mindset message, especially when the stereotype of women underperforming in math was brought to their attention, did significantly worse than their male counterparts; however, no gender difference occurred among the students who had received the growth-mindset message, even when the stereotype about girls was mentioned before the test (Good et al., 2009). This research clearly demonstrates that a growth mindset can help girls achieve in math. Dweck explains: "Students are getting this message that things come easily to people who are geniuses, and only if you're a genius do you make these great discoveries. But more and more research is showing that people who made great contributions struggled. And maybe they enjoyed the struggle, but they struggled. The more we can help kids enjoy that effort rather than feel that it's undermining, the better off they'll be."

A GROWTH MINDSET PROMOTES PERSISTENCE IN STEM

Achievement is one thing, but as we've seen, girls and women are achieving at the same levels as boys and men in math and science by many measures yet are not persisting to the same degree in many STEM fields. Ongoing research by Dweck and her colleagues has shown that a growth mindset promotes not only higher achievement but increased persistence in STEM fields as well. Good, Rattan, and Dweck (2009) followed several hundred women at an elite university through a semester of a calculus class. Women who reported that their classrooms communicated a fixed mindset and that negative stereotypes were widespread showed an eroding sense that they belonged in math during the semester, and they were less likely to express a desire to take math in the future. Women who said that their classrooms promoted a growth mindset were less susceptible to the negative effects of stereotypes, and they were more likely to intend to continue to take math in the future. At the beginning of the semester, no difference was seen in interest, excitement, sense of belonging, or intention to continue in math, but by the end of the study, girls who were continually exposed to the fixed-mindset message along with the stereotype that girls don't do well in math lost interest. Dweck and her colleagues are finding similar results in a current study on girls in middle school. Dweck told AAUW, "In all of our research, we've seen that in a fixed mindset, if you are hit with negative messages, you are much more likely to succumb and lose interest." A growth mindset can help maintain a spark of interest.

But how much difference can a growth mindset make? Aren't some people just born with more ability than others? While Dweck does not deny that there can be "talent differences" among students, she reminds us of the difficulty of measuring individual potential: "I don't know how much of talent—even among prodigies—comes from the fact that a person is born with an ability versus the fact that he or she is fascinated with something and passionate about it and does it all the time. I'm not saying anyone can do anything, but I am saying that we don't know where talent comes from, and we don't know who's capable of what."

MINDSET MATTERS

Dweck's research findings are important for women in STEM, because encountering obstacles and challenging problems is the nature of scientific work. In addition, girls have to cope with the stereotype that they are not as capable as boys in math and science. When girls and women believe they have a fixed amount of intelligence, they are more likely to believe the stereotype, lose confidence, and disengage from STEM as a potential career when they encounter difficulties in their course work. The messages we send girls about the nature of intelligence matter. Eradicating stereotypes is a worthwhile but long-term goal. In the meantime, communicating a growth mindset is a step that educators, parents, and anyone who has contact with girls can take to reduce the effect of stereotypes and increase girls' and women's representation in STEM areas. The more girls and women believe that they can learn what they need to be successful in STEM fields (as opposed to being "gifted"), the more likely they are to actually be successful in STEM fields. Dweck's work demonstrates that girls benefit greatly from shifting their view of mathematics ability from "gift" to "learned skill."

RECOMMENDATIONS

- **Teach children that intellectual skills can be acquired.**

  Teach students that the brain is like a muscle that gets stronger and works better the more it is exercised. Teach students that every time they stretch themselves, work hard, and learn something new, their brain forms new connections, and over time they become smarter. Passion, dedication, and self-improvement—not simply innate talent—are the roads to genius and contribution.

- **Praise children for effort.**

  Praise children for the process they use to arrive at conclusions. It is especially important to give process feedback to the most able students who have often coasted along, gotten good grades, and been praised for their intelligence. These may be the very students who opt out when the work becomes more difficult.

- Talented and gifted programs should send the message that they value growth and learning.

  The danger of the "gifted" label is that it conveys the idea that a student has been bestowed with a "gift" of great ability rather than a dynamic attribute that she or he can develop. Talented and gifted programs should send the message that students are in these programs because they are advanced in certain areas and that the purpose of the programs is to challenge students in ways that will help them further develop and bring their abilities to fruition. Consider changing the name of talented and gifted programs to "challenge" programs or "advanced" programs to emphasize more of a growth mindset and less of a fixed mindset.

- Highlight the struggle.

  Parents and teachers can portray challenges, effort, and mistakes as highly valued. Students with a fixed mindset are threatened by challenges, effort, and mistakes, so they may shy away from challenges, limit their effort, and try to avoid or hide mistakes. Communicate to these students that we value and admire effort, hard work, and learning from mistakes. Teach children the values that are at the heart of scientific and mathematical contributions: love of challenge, love of hard work, and the ability to embrace and learn from our inevitable mistakes. In Dweck's words, "The message needs to be that we value taking on challenges and learning and growth. Educators should highlight the struggle."

Chapter 3.
Stereotypes

> Girls do every bit as well in their graded work [as] boys [do], but girls lose confidence as they advance through the grades and will start to do more poorly than boys on the timed tests, despite getting good grades. One reason for this loss of confidence is the stereotyping that kids are exposed to—in school and the media and even in the home—that portrays boys as more innately gifted [in math]. Without denying the fact that boys may have some biological advantage, I think that psychology plays a big role here.
>
> —Joshua Aronson[4]

Negative stereotypes about girls' and women's abilities in mathematics and science persist despite girls' and women's considerable gains in participation and performance in these areas during the last few decades. Two stereotypes are prevalent: girls are not as good as boys in math, and scientific work is better suited to boys and men. As early as elementary school, children are aware of these stereotypes and can express stereotypical beliefs about which science courses are suitable for females and males (Farenga & Joyce, 1999; Ambady et al., 2001). Research profiled in chapter 8 verifies the prevalence of these stereotypes among adults as well (Nosek et al., 2002b). Furthermore, girls and young women have been found to be aware of, and negatively affected by, the stereotypical image of a scientist as a man (Buck et al., 2008). Although largely unspoken, negative stereotypes about women and girls in STEM are very much alive.

A large body of experimental research has found that negative stereotypes affect women's and girls' performance and aspirations in math and science through a phenomenon called "stereotype threat." Even female students who strongly identify with math—who think that they are good at math and being good in math is important to them—are susceptible to its effects (Nguyen & Ryan, 2008). Stereotype threat may help explain the discrepancy between female students' higher grades in math and science and their lower performance on high-stakes tests in these subjects, such as the SAT-math (SAT-M) and AP calculus exam. Additionally, stereotype threat may also help explain why fewer girls than boys express interest in and aspirations for careers in mathematically demanding fields. Girls may attempt to reduce the likelihood that they will be judged through the lens of negative stereotypes by saying they are not interested and by avoiding these fields.

---

[4]Joshua Aronson is an associate professor of developmental, social, and educational psychology at New York University. His research focuses on the social and psychological influences on academic achievement, and he is internationally known for his research on stereotype threat and minority student achievement. He was the founding director of the Center for Research on Culture, Development, and Education at New York University. His forthcoming book is titled *The Nurture of Intelligence*.

This chapter profiles the research on stereotype threat and women in science and math, highlighting the work of social psychologist Joshua Aronson. In the mid-1990s Aronson and his colleagues Claude Steele and Steven Spencer first identified and described the phenomenon of stereotype threat, the threat of being viewed through the lens of a negative stereotype or the fear of doing something that would confirm that stereotype (Steele & Aronson, 1995). Stereotype threat arises in situations where a negative stereotype is relevant to evaluating performance. For example, a female student taking a math test would experience an extra cognitive and emotional burden of worry related to the stereotype that women are not good at math. A reference to this stereotype, however subtle, could adversely affect her test performance. When the burden is removed, however, her performance would improve.

This phenomenon was first identified in experiments examining factors that could explain differences in academic performance among African American and white college students. Aronson and his colleagues observed that existing research did not fully explain the gaps in academic performance between these groups. In addition to considering factors such as home and family variables, school-related variables, and peer influences, Aronson and his colleagues believed that psychological factors at the student level needed to be considered. Their theory focused on the psychological predicament rooted in stereotypical images of certain groups as intellectually inferior. They referred to this phenomenon as stereotype threat and offered it as an important factor—albeit not the sole factor—producing group differences in test performance and academic motivation.

Stereotype threat can be felt as both psychological and physiological responses that result in impaired performance. For example, Blascovich et al. (2001) found that African Americans taking an intelligence test under stereotype threat had higher blood pressure levels than whites did. No difference in blood pressure levels of African Americans and whites occurred in the nonthreat situation. Steele and Aronson (1995) found that stereotyped individuals often made more of an effort (attempted the same number of items if not more) than nonthreatened participants did but reread items more often and worked slower with less accuracy.

In one of the earliest experiments looking specifically at women, Spencer et al. (1999) recruited 30 female and 24 male first-year University of Michigan psychology students with strong math backgrounds and similar math abilities as measured by grades and test scores. All students strongly identified with math. The students were divided into two groups, and the researchers administered a math test on computers using items from the math section of the Graduate Record Exam. One group was told that men performed better than women on the test (the threat condition), and the other group was told that there were no gender differences in test performance (the nonthreat condition). Spencer et al. believed that if stereotype threat could explain gender differences in performance, then presenting the test as

Figure 15. Performance on a Challenging Math Test, by Stereotype Threat Condition and Gender

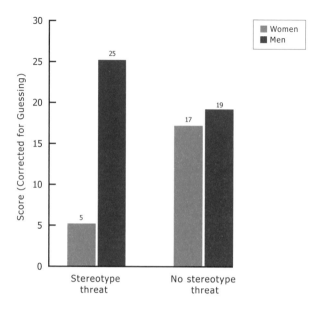

Source: Spencer et al., 1999, "Stereotype threat and women's math performance," *Journal of Experimental Social Psychology, 35*(1), p. 13.

free of gender bias would remove the stereotype threat, and women would perform as well as men. If, however, gender differences in performance were due to sex-linked ability differences in math, women would perform worse than men even when the stereotype threat had been lifted. They found that women performed significantly worse than men in the threat situation and that the gender difference almost disappeared in the nonthreat condition (see figure 15).

In the ensuing decade more than 300 studies have been published that support this finding. The results of these experiments show that stereotype threat is often the default situation in testing environments. The threat can be easily induced by asking students to indicate their gender before a test or simply having a larger ratio of men to women in a testing situation (Inzlicht & Ben-Zeev, 2000). Research consistently finds that stereotype threat adversely affects women's math performance to a modest degree (Nguyen & Ryan, 2008) and may account for as much as 20 points on the math portion of the SAT (Walton & Spencer, 2009). While 20 points on a test with a total possible score of 800 may seem small, in 2008 the average male score on the SAT math exam was 30 points higher than the average female score, so eliminating stereotype threat could eliminate two-thirds of the gender gap on the SAT-M.

Aronson's research also has shown that high-achieving and motivated women in the pipeline to STEM majors and careers are susceptible to stereotype threat. Aronson conducted a field experiment at a large public university in the southwest to investigate stereotype threat among students in a high-level calculus course that is a pipeline to future careers in science. The results showed no difference in performance between female and male STEM majors when they were told that a difficult math test was a diagnosis of their ability (threat condition); however, when the threat was removed by telling the students that women and men performed equally well on the test, the women performed significantly better than the men (Good et al., 2008).

Stereotype threat also has implications beyond test performance. In an interview with AAUW, Aronson suggested that one reason girls lose confidence as they advance in school stems from "the stereotyping that students are exposed to in school, the media, and even at home that portrays boys as more innately gifted and math as a gift rather than a developed skill. Without denying that biological factors may play a role in some math domains, psychology also plays a big role." Additionally, a repeated or long-term threat can eventually undermine aspirations in the area of interest through a process called "disidentification." Aronson describes disidentification as a defense to avoid the risk of being judged by a stereotype. Faced with a stereotype that girls are not good at math, for example, an individual might respond by claiming, "I don't care about math; it's not who I am." In extreme cases, rather than repeatedly confronting a negative stereotype, girls and women might avoid the stereotype by avoiding math and science altogether.

Fortunately, Aronson and others have shown that stereotype threat can be alleviated by teaching students about it (Johns et al., 2005), reassuring students that tests are fair (Good et al., 2003), and exposing students to female role models in math and science (McIntyre et al., 2003, 2005). Another promising approach draws on the work of Carol Dweck, profiled in the previous chapter. Encouraging students to think of their math abilities as expandable can lift stereotype threat and have a significant positive effect on students' grades and test scores (Aronson et al., 2002; Good et al., 2003). In the interview with AAUW, Aronson stressed that "exposing students to role models who can help students see their struggles as a normal part of the learning process rather than as a signal of low ability" can boost the test scores of both minority students and girls.

RECOMMENDATIONS

- Encourage students to have a more flexible or growth mindset about intelligence.

  Interventions designed to help students adopt a malleable mindset about intelligence and thus reduce their vulnerability to stereotype threat positively affect their academic performance.

- Expose girls to successful female role models in math and science.

  Exposing girls to successful female role models can help counter negative stereotypes because girls see that people like them can be successful and stereotype threat can be managed and overcome.

- Teach students and teachers about stereotype threat.

  Research with college students shows that acknowledging and explicitly teaching students about stereotype threat can result in better performance. Teachers and college faculty are best suited to do this and, therefore, need to be educated about stereotype threat.

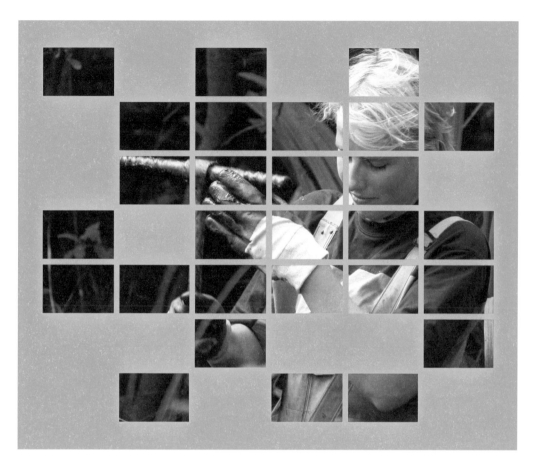

Chapter 4.
Self-Assessment

> Boys do not pursue mathematical activities at a higher rate than girls do because they are better at mathematics. They do so, at least partially, because they *think* they are better.
>
> —Shelley Correll[5] [emphasis added]

Fewer girls than boys say they are interested in science or engineering careers (American Society for Quality, 2009; WGBH, 2009). The work of Shelley Correll, a sociologist at Stanford University, sheds light on how girls' and women's seemingly voluntary decisions to avoid STEM careers are influenced by the cultural belief that science and math are male domains. Correll's research focuses on self-assessment and its consequences for interest in math and science. She found that among students with equivalent past achievement in math, boys assessed their mathematical ability higher than girls did. Controlling for actual ability, the higher students assessed their mathematical ability, the greater the odds were that they would enroll in a high school calculus course and choose a college major in science, math, or engineering. Correll found that boys were more likely than their equally accomplished female peers to enroll in calculus not because boys were better at math but because they believed that they were better at math. When mathematical self-assessment levels were controlled, the previous higher enrollment of boys in calculus disappeared and the gender gap in college major choice was reduced (Correll, 2001). In a follow-up study Correll (2004) verified in a laboratory experiment that when cultural beliefs about male superiority exist in any area, even a fictitious one, girls assess their abilities in that area lower, judge themselves by a higher standard, and express less of a desire to pursue a career in that area than boys do.

Undoubtedly, many factors influence an individual's career choice, but at a minimum, individuals must believe they have the ability to succeed in a given career to develop preferences for that career. If girls do not believe they have the ability to become a scientist or engineer, they will choose to be something else. Correll's research findings suggest that helping girls understand that girls and boys are equally capable in STEM areas will increase girls' self-assessment of their math and science skills, which, in turn, will increase girls' aspirations for careers in STEM fields.

Correll first became interested in the differences between boys' and girls' assessments of their science and math abilities when she taught high school chemistry for a few years before attending graduate school. She noticed that no matter how poorly the boys in her chemistry

---

[5]Shelley Correll is an associate professor of sociology at Stanford University. Her research examines how cultural beliefs about gender influence educational and career paths. In addition to her work on self-assessment described in this chapter, her most recent project considers how stereotypical beliefs associated with motherhood influence the workplace evaluations, pay, and hiring of women who give evidence of being a mother.

classes did, they continued to think that they were very good at chemistry; however, no matter how well the girls performed, it was difficult for Correll to convince them that they actually had some scientific ability. Once in graduate school Correll focused on how gender stereotypes attached to different skills or tasks influence how girls and boys understand their abilities independent of test scores or grades and how these gender differences in self-assessments contribute to gender differences in career choice.

STEREOTYPES AND SELF-ASSESSMENTS

How do stereotypes affect self-assessments? Correll explains that we use stereotypes as "cognitive crutches" in situations in which we do not know how to judge our performance. Research shows that even individuals who do not personally endorse beliefs that men are better than women at math are likely to be aware that these beliefs exist in the culture and expect that others will treat them according to these beliefs. This expectation, or what we think "most people" believe, has been shown to influence judgments (Foschi, 1996; Steele, 1997; Lovaglia et al., 1998). If a girl believes that most people, especially those in her immediate environment, think boys are better than girls at math, that thought is going to affect her, even if she doesn't believe it herself. Even if no one really believes that boys are better at math, the fact that a girl thinks they believe it is what matters. This is the reason that the 2005 comments of Larry Summers—the former Harvard president who famously doubted that women are capable of succeeding at the highest levels of science and engineering—were so damaging. Because he spoke from such a powerful position, his remarks gave credibility to the stereotype that women may lack the aptitude to succeed in STEM fields.

Correll published a study in 2001 that looked at the correlation between students' math achievement and self-assessment of their math ability by gender and the influence that self-assessment has on persistence on a path to a STEM career. This study analyzed the National Educational Longitudinal Study of 1988 (NELS-88), a national dataset of more than 16,000 high school students. The first NELS-88 survey was conducted in 1988 when the students were in the eighth grade. A subsample of the original students was again surveyed in 1990, 1992, and 1994, when most were sophomores, seniors, and two years beyond high school, respectively.

Correll identified three items on the survey as indicators of mathematical self-assessment: "Mathematics is one of my best subjects," "I have always done well in math," and "I get good marks in math." Students were asked to agree or disagree, on a six-point scale, with these statements during their sophomore year of high school. Student mathematical achievement was approximated through past math test scores and average math grades that students received in high school. Correll's analysis showed that high school boys were more likely than their female counterparts of equal past mathematical performance to believe that they were competent at mathematics. Interestingly, the effect was reversed when the students assessed their verbal ability: female students made significantly higher self-assessments of verbal ability, controlling for actual verbal performance. This suggests that stereotypes about gender influence students' perceptions of their abilities in particular fields: boys do not assess their task competence higher than girls do in every area, just in the areas considered to be masculine domains.

Most important for understanding how gender differences in self-assessment influence women's underrepresentation in science and engineering, Correll's research found that higher mathematical self-assessment among students of equal abilities increased students' odds of enrolling in high school calculus and choosing a quantitative college major. In her sample, she found that boys were 1.2 times more likely than their equally capable female counterparts to enroll in calculus. Correll found this difference to be due to differences in self-assessment. When girls and boys assessed themselves as equally mathematically competent, the gender difference disappeared, and girls and boys were equally likely to enroll in calculus. Likewise, 4 percent of female students compared with 12 percent of male students in Correll's sample chose a college major in engineering, mathematics, or the physical sciences. Although controlling for mathematical self-assessment did not eliminate this gender difference in college major choice, it did reduce the difference. Together these findings suggest that cultural beliefs about the appropriateness of one career choice over another can influence self-assessment and partially account for the disproportionately high numbers of men in the quantitative professions, over and above measures of actual ability (Correll, 2001).

Interestingly, Correll found that young women who enrolled in high school calculus were about three times more likely than young women who did not take calculus to choose a quantitative major in college. In comparison, young men who enrolled in calculus were only about twice as likely as young men who did not take calculus to choose a quantitative major. Thus it appears that taking calculus in high school is a better predictor of selecting a quantitative college major for women than it is for men. Another interesting finding was that higher verbal self-assessments decreased the odds of enrolling in calculus and choosing a quantitative major, indicating that students use relative understandings of their competencies when making career-relevant decisions. Lubinski and Benbow (2006) showed that girls who do very well at math are more likely than their male peers to do very well at verbal tasks as well. In addition to societal expectations, relatively strong verbal abilities may encourage mathematically talented girls to consider future education and careers in the humanities or social sciences rather than science and engineering fields.

In a follow-up study Correll (2004) tested her theory that boys assess their abilities higher and express higher aspirations to pursue a career in areas considered to be male domains in an experimental setting. She conducted this experiment to show that cultural beliefs about gender, not actual gender differences, influence self-assessments about math. The previous study relied on the assumption that the students in the sample were aware of the cultural beliefs about gender and mathematical abilities, and this awareness caused the observed gender differences in self-assessments of competence. Since Correll could not isolate and manipulate students' exposure to gender beliefs associated with these abilities in that study, however, she could not be sure that cultural beliefs about gender caused the difference in self-assessment and not, for example, some additional component of "real" mathematical ability not captured by math grades and test scores. To account for this possibility, Correll designed an experiment around a fictitious skill called "contrast sensitivity ability." In this experiment, participants were given evidence that contrast sensitivity ability (the ability to detect proportions of how much black and white appeared on a screen) was either an ability that men were more likely to have (male advantage or "MA" condition) or an ability that showed no gender difference (gender dissociated or "GD" condition). Participants included 80 first-year undergraduate students divided into four groups: 20 men and 20 women in the MA group and 20 men and 20 women in the GD group.

Participants completed two 20-item rounds of a computer-administered contrast-sensitivity test in which subjects had five seconds to judge which color (black or white) predominated in each of a series of rectangles. Unbeknownst to the subjects, the amount of white and black was either exactly equal or very close to equal in each rectangle, so the test had no right or wrong answers. Nonetheless, all subjects were told that they had correctly answered 13 of the 20 items during round one and 12 of 20 in round two. Participants were then asked to assess their performance and indicate their interest in pursuing a career requiring contrast-sensitivity ability.

In the MA group, men assessed their contrast-sensitivity ability and their interest in pursuing careers requiring this ability higher than women did, even though all participants received identical scores on the tests. Because the test had no right answers, men could not really be better at the contrast-sensitivity task; yet when told that men excelled at this ability, they assessed their own abilities higher than women assessed their own abilities and expressed more interest than women did in using this ability in a future career. When Correll controlled for level of self-assessment, a gender difference no longer existed in aspirations for a career requiring high contrast-sensitivity ability, which suggests that higher self-assessment among the men led them to express more interest than women did in using this ability in a future career. In the GD group, where the fictitious skill was described as equally likely to be held by women and men, no gender differences appeared in assessments of ability or interest in using the skill in the future (Correll, 2004) (see figure 16).

Perhaps the most interesting finding from this study is that women and men held different standards for what constituted high ability in the MA condition. In the MA condition, women believed they had to earn a score of at least 89 percent to be successful, but men felt that a minimum score of 79 percent was sufficient to be successful— a difference of 10 percentage points. In the GD condition, women and men had much more similar ideas about how high their scores would have to be to assess themselves as having high task ability: women said they would need to score 82 percent, while men said they would need to score 83 percent (see figure 17). This finding suggests that women hold themselves to a higher standard than their male peers do in "masculine" fields.

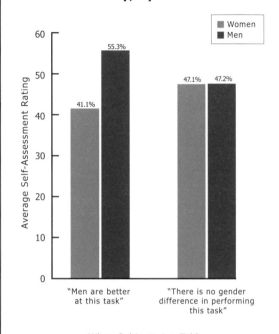

Figure 16. Self-Assessment of Ability, by Gender

Source: Correll, S. J., 2004, "Constraints into preferences: Gender, status, and emerging career aspirations," *American Sociological Review, 69,* p. 106, Table 2.

Correll's findings suggest that the mere fact that science, technology, engineering, and mathematics are commonly considered to be masculine domains may increase men's self-assessment of their abilities and interest and lower women's self-assessment and interest in pursuing careers in these areas. Additionally, the research indicates that women believe that they must achieve at exceptionally high levels in math and science to be successful STEM professionals. If women hold themselves to a higher standard than men do, fewer women than men of equal ability will assess themselves as being good at math and science and aspire to science and engineering careers.

Fortunately, the findings also suggest that it is possible to alter the standards individuals use by altering the beliefs in their local environments. In the study, none of the participants had ever heard about contrast-sensitivity ability, so no one had preconceived ideas about it.

Figure 17. Students' Standards for Their Own Performance, by Gender

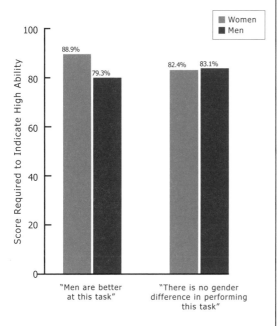

Legend: ■ Women ■ Men

Y-axis: Score Required to Indicate High Ability (0, 20, 40, 60, 80, 100)

"Men are better at this task" — Women: 88.9%, Men: 79.3%
"There is no gender difference in performing this task" — Women: 82.4%, Men: 83.1%

X-axis label: When Subjects Are Told ...

Note: Respondents were asked, "How high would you have to score to be convinced that you have high ability at this task?"
Source: Correll, S. J., 2004, "Constraints into preferences: Gender, status, and emerging career aspirations," *American Sociological Review, 69,* p. 106, Table 2.

Yet when participants were told that men are better at the task, women used a higher standard to assess their abilities than the standard men used to assess themselves. When participants were told that no gender difference existed in task performance, the gender difference went away, and women and men assessed themselves by nearly the same standard. This suggests that people—teachers and parents in particular—have an opportunity to affect the standards that girls and boys and women and men use and, therefore, the assessments that they make by emphasizing the lack of gender difference in performance in nearly every STEM subject.

As mentioned previously, fewer girls than boys say they are interested in becoming scientists or engineers. But how do girls form interests and career aspirations? Individuals form career aspirations in part by drawing on perceptions of their own competence at career-relevant tasks. Correll's research shows that the cultural association of mathematical competence with boys and men negatively influences girls' self-assessments compared with boys' and raises the standard by which they judge themselves. Girls' lower self-assessment of their math ability, even in the face of good grades and test scores, contributes to fewer girls expressing preference for and aspiring to STEM careers. In this way, belief structures in the general culture influence individual choices, and those who decide to pursue STEM careers may not be those who are best qualified for careers requiring mathematical ability.

RECOMMENDATIONS

Correll's research shows that the environment and culture around girls influences their self-assessment, so her recommendations for change focus on changing the environment. As Correll explained in an interview with AAUW:

Enhancing how girls feel about themselves is very, very important, but if we don't do the flip side, and change how other people feel about girls, we're setting girls up to feel good about themselves only to encounter structures that are really pretty negative for them.

Research shows a number of direct, immediate ways to help girls better assess their math skills:

- **Schools, departments, and workplaces can cultivate a culture of respect.**

  Correll's research shows that people respond not so much to widely held stereotypes in the larger culture but to the stereotypes that are operating in their immediate environment. When institutions (including K–12 schools, universities, and work-places) and individuals send the message that girls and boys are equally capable of achieving in math and science, girls are more likely to assess their abilities more accurately. Since schools are responsible for educating, they have a unique opportunity to help students learn new ways to interact. By teaching students to recognize stereotypes, teachers can cultivate a culture of respect in their classrooms.

- **Teachers and professors can reduce reliance on stereotypes by making performance standards and expectations clear.**

  The same letter or number grade on an assignment or exam might signal something different to girls than it does to boys. By using phrases like, "If you got above an 80 on this test, you are doing a great job in this class," teachers help students understand their grades so that students don't have to rely on stereotypes to create a standard for themselves. The more that teachers and professors can reduce uncertainty about students' performance, the less students will rely on stereotypes to assess themselves.

- **Encourage high school girls to take calculus, physics, chemistry, computer science, and engineering classes when available.**

  Correll's 2001 study showed that girls who took calculus in high school were more than three times as likely as girls who did not take calculus in high school to major in a STEM field in college. Taking higher-level science and math classes in high school keeps STEM options open.

Chapter 5.
Spatial Skills

> Most engineering faculty have highly developed 3-D spatial skills and may not understand that others can struggle with a topic they find so easy. Furthermore, they may not believe that spatial skills can be improved through practice, falsely believing that this particular skill is one that a person is either "born with" or not. They don't understand that they probably developed these skills over many years.
>
> —Sheryl Sorby[6]

One of the most persistent gender gaps in cognitive skills is found in the area of spatial skills, specifically on measures of mental rotation, where researchers consistently find that men outscore women by a medium to large margin (Linn & Petersen, 1985; Voyer et al., 1995). While no definitive evidence proves that strong spatial abilities are required for achievement in STEM careers (Ceci et al., 2009), many people, including science and engineering professors, view them as important for success in fields like engineering and classes like organic chemistry. The National Academy of Sciences states that "spatial thinking is at the heart of many great discoveries in science, that it underpins many of the activities of the modern workforce, and that it pervades the everyday activities of modern life" (National Research Council, Committee on Support for Thinking Spatially, 2006, p.1).

Sheryl Sorby, a professor of mechanical engineering and engineering mechanics at Michigan Technological University, has studied the role of spatial-skills training in the retention of female students in engineering since the early 1990s. She finds that individuals can dramatically improve their 3-D spatial-visualization skills within a short time with training, and female engineering students with poorly developed spatial skills who receive spatial-visualization training are more likely to stay in engineering than are their peers who do not receive training.

Sorby became interested in the topic of spatial skills through her personal difficulty with spatial tasks as an engineering student. In an interview with AAUW, Sorby described her experience:

> I was blessed with the ability to do academic work. When I got to college, I was getting A's in all of my classes, getting 97 on chemistry exams where the average was in the 50s, and then my second quarter, I took this engineering graphics course, and it was the first time in my entire life

---

[6]Sheryl Sorby is a professor of mechanical engineering and engineering mechanics and director of the engineering education and innovation research group at Michigan Technological University. Her research interests include graphics and visualization. She serves as an associate editor of the American Society for Engineering Education's new online journal, *Advances in Engineering Education*.

that I couldn't do something in an academic setting. I was really frustrated, and I worked harder on that class than I did on my calculus and my chemistry classes combined.

A few years later, when Sorby was working on a doctorate in engineering, she found herself teaching the same course that she had struggled with: "While I was teaching this class, it seemed anecdotally to me that a lot of young women had the same issues with this class that I had had. They just struggled, they didn't know what they were doing, they were frustrated, and I had a number of them tell me: 'I'm leaving engineering because I can't do this. I really shouldn't be here.'"

After she earned a doctorate in engineering mechanics in the early 1990s, Sorby connected with Beverly Baartmans, a math educator at Michigan Tech, who introduced her to research on gender differences in spatial cognition, and Sorby began to understand her own and her students' challenges with spatial visualization in a new way. As a result, Sorby and Baartmans formulated the following research question: *If spatial skills are critical to success in engineering graphics, and graphics is one of the first engineering courses that students take, and women's spatial skills lag behind those of their male counterparts, will women become discouraged in this introductory course at a disproportionate rate and drop out of engineering as a result?*

To answer this question, Sorby and Baartmans, with funding from the National Science Foundation, developed a course in spatial visualization for first-year engineering students who had poorly developed spatial skills. The researchers' intention was to increase the retention of women in engineering through this course, which focused on teaching basic spatial-visualization skills, including isometric and orthographic sketching, rotation and reflection of objects, and cross sections of solids.

In one of their first studies in 1993, Sorby and Baartmans administered the Purdue Spatial Visualization Test: Rotations (PSVT:R) (Guay, 1977) along with a background questionnaire to 535 first-year Michigan Tech engineering students during orientation. An example from the PSVT:R is shown in figure 18. Sorby's analysis of the results of the test and the background questionnaire showed that previous experience in design-related courses such as drafting, mechanical drawing, and art, as well as play as children with construction toys such as Legos, Lincoln Logs, and Erector Sets, predicted good performance on the PSVT:R. Another factor that predicted success was being a man. Women were more than three times as likely as their male peers to fail the test, with 39 percent of the women failing the test compared with 12 percent of the men (Sorby & Baartmans, 2000).

Figure 18. Sample Question from the Purdue Spatial Visualization Test: Rotations (PSVT:R)

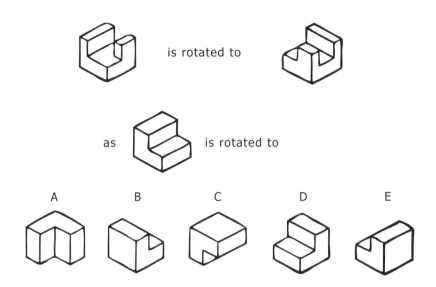

is rotated to

as   is rotated to

A   B   C   D   E

Note: The correct answer is D.
Source: Guay, R., 1977, Purdue Spatial Visualization Test: Rotations (West Lafayette, IN: Purdue Research Foundation), reproduced in Sorby, S. A., 2009, "Educational research in developing 3-D spatial skills for engineering students," International Journal of Science Education, 31(3), p. 463.

IMPROVING SPATIAL SKILLS

Sorby then selected a random sample of 24 students (11 women and 13 men) who failed the PSVT:R test to participate in the pilot offering of the spatial-visualization course. During a 10-week period, these students took a three-credit course that included two hours of lecture and a two-hour computer lab each week. Lectures covered topics such as cross sections of solids, sketching multiview drawings of simple objects, and paper folding to illustrate 2-D to 3-D transformations. In the lab, students used solid-modeling computer-aided design (CAD) software to illustrate the principles presented during the lectures. At the end of the course, students took the PSVT:R again. The results were remarkable. Students' test scores improved from an average score of 52 percent on the PSVT:R before taking the class to 82 percent after taking it. This is approximately 10 times the improvement that would be expected of someone taking the PSVT:R a second time with no training (ibid.) and three to four times the improvement that Sorby had seen among her students as a result of taking an engineering-graphics or computer-design course. Sorby is quick to point out that her course does not help people become perfect at spatial visualization; rather, the training brings students' scores up to the average score for all engineering students. This finding is particularly relevant for women in STEM fields because, although no gender differences appeared in average pre- or post-test scores among the students taking the course, as explained above, a much larger percentage of women failed the test initially.

Sorby and her colleagues continued to offer this course through 1999 to engineering freshmen who failed the PSVT:R. Each year, students' scores on the PSVT:R increased by 20 to 32 percentage points on average after taking the course. In 2000 Sorby condensed the training into a one-credit course that met once each week for 14 weeks for a two-hour lab session. She found similar results: students' PSVT:R scores increased 26 percentage points on average after the training among the 186 students who took the course between 2000 and 2002 (Sorby, 2009).

In 2004 and 2005 Sorby conducted a study with nonengineering first-year students at Michigan Tech and pilot studies with high school and middle school students and in each case found that students' spatial scores improved with training. Other universities, such as Virginia Tech and Purdue, are now offering the spatial-visualization course, and the National Science Foundation has funded the Women in Engineering ProActive Network (WEPAN) to make the course available to students at 30 additional universities by 2014. Sorby, along with Baartmans and Anne Wysocki, published a multimedia software-workbook package, *Introduction to 3D Spatial Visualization*, in 2003, which contains content similar to the course and is available to the general public to guide anyone interested in improving her or his 3-D spatial visualization skills.

IMPROVING RETENTION

Sorby has produced striking findings on spatial skills and retention of female engineering students. She found that among the women who initially failed the PSVT:R and took the spatial-visualization course between 1993 and 1998, 77 percent (69 out of 90) were still enrolled in or had graduated from the school of engineering. In comparison only 48 percent (77 out of 161) of the women who initially failed the PSVT:R and did not take Sorby's course were still enrolled or had graduated from the school of engineering.

Much of Sorby's analysis is based on nonrandom samples of students since, after the first year, students opted to take the course rather than being randomly assigned. Therefore, the women who remained in engineering after taking the course may have been more motivated to succeed in engineering to begin with, and the higher retention rate could be a result of their motivation rather than the course. Nonetheless, Sorby's findings were consistent and compelling enough to convince the departmental chairs and the dean at Michigan Tech to require the spatial-skills course for all students who fail the PSVT:R during orientation, starting in fall 2009. Sorby will soon be able to isolate the impact of the course itself on retention since all students who fail the test are now required to take the course, and the students are no longer self-selected.

Sorby believes that well-developed spatial skills can help retain women in engineering and help attract more girls to STEM. She sees well-developed spatial skills as important for creating confidence in one's ability to succeed in math and science courses and ultimately in a STEM career, because spatial skills are needed to interpret diagrams and drawings in math and science textbooks as early as elementary school. In a pilot study Sorby found that middle school girls who took a spatial-visualization course took more advanced-level math and science courses in high school than did girls who did not take the course. Sorby recommends that this training happen by middle school or earlier to make a difference in girls' choices.

Sorby's research shows that with training, women and men achieve consistent and large gains in tests of spatial skills. First-year engineering students, undergraduate students outside engineering, high school students, and middle school students have all shown improvement with training. Sorby's work demonstrates that spatial skills can indeed be developed through practice.

RECOMMENDATIONS

Parents, AAUW volunteers, and teachers, especially engineering educators, can help young people, especially girls, develop their spatial skills in the following ways:

- Explain to young people that spatial skills are not innate but developed.

- Encourage children and students to play with construction toys, take things apart and put them back together again, play games that involve fitting objects into different places, draw, and work with their hands.

- Use handheld models when possible (rather than computer models) to help students visualize what they see on paper in front of them.

Chapter 6.
The College Student Experience

Many young women graduate from high school with the skills needed to succeed in majors in science, technology, engineering, and mathematics, yet college-bound women are less likely than men to pursue majors in these fields (National Science Board, 2010). The culture of academic departments in colleges and universities has been identified as a critical issue for women's success in earning college degrees in STEM fields (National Academy of Sciences, 2007). This chapter profiles two research projects that demonstrate how improving the culture in science and engineering departments can help keep capable female students enrolled in these majors.

Jane Margolis and Allan Fisher's research on women in computer science at Carnegie Mellon University and Barbara Whitten's work on women in college physics departments found departmental culture to be a key factor in female students' decision to remain in or leave these majors. Both projects provide practical ideas for improving the climate at college for female students in STEM. These researchers demonstrate that small changes in recruitment, admissions, and course work and creating and promoting opportunities for positive interactions among students and between students and faculty can make a big difference in students' experiences.

CULTURE OF A COMPUTER SCIENCE DEPARTMENT

Margolis and Fisher conducted a four-year study of women and computing at the School of Computer Science at Carnegie Mellon University, one of the premiere schools of computer science in the United States. Between 1995 and 1999 they interviewed more than 100 students multiple times, beginning with the student's first semester in the computer science department and concluding when the student either graduated or left the major. Margolis and Fisher also held discussions with faculty, examined student journals, and observed classes. At the beginning of their study, women made up only 7 percent of the undergraduate computer

---

[7]Jane Margolis is a senior researcher at the UCLA Graduate School of Education and Information Studies. Through her studies of the gender and race gap in computer science, she examines social inequities in education and how fields become segregated. She is the co-author of two award-winning books, *Unlocking the Clubhouse: Women in Computing* (MIT Press, 2002) and *Stuck in the Shallow End: Education, Race, and Computing* (MIT Press, 2008). Allan Fisher is vice president for product strategy and development at the Laureate Higher Education Group. He served until 1999 as faculty member and associate dean for undergraduate education in the School of Computer Science at Carnegie Mellon University and wrote *Unlocking the Clubhouse: Women in Computing* with Jane Margolis.

science majors and were almost twice as likely as men were to leave the major (Margolis & Fisher, 2002). As the associate dean for undergraduate computer science education, Fisher was concerned about the attrition of female majors. Margolis was a social scientist with a background in gender and education and an interest in how fields become segregated and was intrigued to understand why so few women study computer science. Margolis and Fisher characterize their work as an "insider-outsider" collaboration.

Departmental culture includes the expectations, assumptions, and values that guide the actions of professors, staff, and students. Individuals may or may not be aware of the influence of departmental culture as they design and teach classes, advise students, organize activities, and take classes. Margolis and Fisher described how the computing culture reflects the norms, desires, and interests of a subset of males—those who take an early interest in computing and pursue it with passion during adolescence and into college. Margolis and Fisher point out that throughout the life cycle "computing is actively claimed as 'guy stuff' by boys and men and passively ceded by girls and women" (ibid., p. 4). This pattern of behavior is influenced by external forces in U.S. culture that associate success in computing more with boys and men than with girls and women and often makes women feel that they don't belong simply because of their gender. In an interview with AAUW, Margolis explained: "There is a subset of boys and men who burn with a passion for computers and computing. Through the intensity of their interest, they both mark the field as male and enshrine in its culture their preference for single-minded intensity and focus on technology." Within that environment this particular male model of "doing" computer science becomes the measure of success; however, because young women and men often have different experiences with computers and different motivations to study computer science, this model can alienate women.

Many young men in computer science report having had an immediate and strong engagement with the computer from an early age. That engagement intensified in middle and high school and led the young men to declare a computer science major. On the other hand, many women who are interested in computer science and have similar talent do not report a similar experience. Many of these young women report a more moderate interest in computer science, especially early on, that builds gradually. Distinguishing between an interest in computer science and an interest in computers and technology is important. Historically girls had less interest in and experience both with computers and in computer science. Today women and men are interested in and equally likely to use computers and technology for educational and communication purposes (Singh et al., 2007), but the gender gap in the study of computer science remains.

About three-quarters of the men that Margolis and Fisher interviewed fit the profile of someone with an intense and immediate attraction to computing that started at a young age, in contrast to about one-quarter of the women in their study. Fisher explained, "There is a dominant culture of 'this is how you do computer science,' and if you do not fit that image, that shakes confidence and interest in continuing." According to Margolis and Fisher (2002, p. 72), "A critical part of attracting more girls and women in computer science is providing multiple ways to 'be in' computer science."

Other researchers concur that feeling like a misfit can lower confidence, especially among women. Female undergraduates often report lower confidence than male undergraduates report in their math or science abilities and their ability to succeed in their STEM major (Seymour & Hewitt, 1997; Cohoon & Aspray, 2006). Even among women and men who have similar grades, women in computer-related majors are less confident than their male peers of their ability to succeed in their major (Singh et al., 2007). Margolis and Fisher also found that the group of female computer science majors who were brimming with confidence and excitement about their major in the earliest interviews were no longer "buzzing" by the second and third semester. Margolis and Fisher (2002, p. 92) argue, "The decline in women's confidence must be acknowledged as an institutional problem."

Curriculum can also play a role in signaling who belongs in the major. Computer science programs often focus on technical aspects of programming early in the curriculum and leave the broader applications for later. This can be a deterrent to students, both female and male, who may be interested in broader, multidisciplinary applications and especially to women, who are more likely to report interest in these broader applications. As with many changes, Margolis and Fisher found that many men, as well as women, might benefit from a redesigned computing curriculum. In their interviews with Margolis and Fisher, male computer science majors also expressed an interest in the broader applications of computer science; therefore, the researchers argue that defining computer science broadly expands its appeal to both women and men. In an interview with AAUW, Margolis emphasized:

> It is really important to redefine or re-envision [what we mean by computer science] because for so long people thought of computer science as focused on the machine and hacking away at the computer. But computer science is now a discipline that is playing a key role in invention and creation across all sorts of disciplines from biological science to film and animation, and that expansion of the field and how critical it is across all disciplines increasingly makes it more meaningful.

Culture can also influence what faculty, students, and others in the department believe a computer science major should look like. The iconic image of the computer science major was for many years the asocial "geek"—a person in love with computers, myopically focused on them to the neglect of all else, at the computer 24/7. Although Margolis and Fisher found that female and male students agreed that the overwhelming image of a computer science major at Carnegie Mellon is the geek, more than two-thirds of the women and almost one-third of the men said that the image did not fit them. Yet the geek image was especially damaging to women. One-fifth of the women interviewed questioned whether they belonged in computer science because they did not have that intense connection and focus that they observed in their male peers. According to Margolis and Fisher (2002, p. 71), "The rub for women in computer science is that the dominant computer science culture does not venerate balance of multiple interests. Instead the singular and obsessive interest in computing that is common among men is assumed to be the road to success in computing. This model shapes the assumptions of who will succeed and who 'belongs' in the discipline."

Today Margolis and Fisher agree that the geek image has evolved since they concluded their study. As computers and computing have become integrated into other disciplines like digital media, including music and film, the geek image has shifted from that of a socially isolated person to include a chic geek image where it can be cool to know about computers and computing. "Nevertheless, although the geek image and focus have softened, it is still an issue that departments deal with," Margolis and Fisher said in the AAUW interview.

These factors—the expectations that go along with being a computer geek, coupled with a male-dominated environment and the focus on programming or hacking—can all contribute to an environment and culture that are major deterrents to the recruitment and retention of women. Margolis and Fisher (2002, p. 6) insist that the goal should not be to fit "women into computer science but rather to change computer science." The majority of the women interviewed, including those who remained in computer science, expressed dissatisfaction with the culture of the discipline. Margolis and Fisher stress that departments should pay attention to the student experience to improve recruitment and retention of women and that having diverse faculty is also critical (see figure 19).

As a result of Margolis and Fisher's work, the School of Computer Science at Carnegie Mellon implemented several changes that helped create a more welcoming culture and improved the recruitment and retention of female students. The proportion of incoming female students increased from 7 percent in 1995, the first year of the study, to 42 percent in 2000. Retention of women also improved during that period (Margolis & Fisher, 2002).

Figure 19. Process for Improving Recruitment and Retention of Women in Computer Science

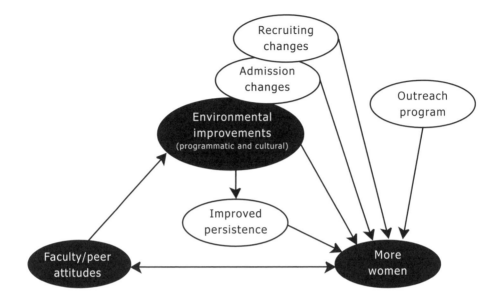

Source: Margolis, J., & Fisher, A., 2002, *Unlocking the clubhouse: Women in computing* (Cambridge: Massachusetts Institute of Technology), p. 139.

RECOMMENDATIONS

Margolis and Fisher offer computer science departments the following recommendations. These could also apply to departments in other STEM disciplines that want to attract and retain diverse and talented students.

- **Perform outreach to high schools.**

    From 1997 to 1999 Carnegie Mellon University hosted a summer institute for advanced placement computer science teachers to prepare them to teach programming and provide them with gender equity instruction to help increase the number of girls taking high school computer science. Not only did participating teachers report success in recruiting more girls, but an increasing number of talented students, both female and male, from the participating high schools applied to the Carnegie Mellon School of Computer Science, which supported the university's recruitment of a more diverse student population.

- **Send an inclusive message about who makes a good computer science student.**

  Carnegie Mellon changed the admissions policy that gave preference to applicants with a lot of previous programming experience once the university realized that this was not a key to student success. This change sent a more inclusive message about who could be a successful computer science student and helped Carnegie Mellon recruit more women with no change in the quality of the applicant pool.

- **Address peer culture.**

  Peer culture within a department has a tremendous effect on students' experiences and is determined primarily by how students treat and relate to one another. Faculty should, therefore, pay attention to peer culture to ensure that no student clique (for example, hackers) dominates or becomes the ideal way of being in the major.

- **Broaden the scope of early course work.**

  Offer introductory courses that show the wide variety of computer science applications and a curricular pathway to complete the degree that does not assume years of computer science experience.

WHAT WORKS FOR WOMEN IN UNDERGRADUATE PHYSICS?

Departmental culture can also be a barrier to women in physics. Physics continues to be one of the most male-dominated of the STEM disciplines, with women earning only 21 percent of bachelor's degrees in 2006 (National Science Foundation, 2008). Barbara Whitten,[8] a professor of physics and women's studies, collaborated with a team of researchers to examine what works for women in undergraduate physics departments.

Whitten began her study in late 2002. For the first phase of the study, she and her colleagues visited nine undergraduate-only physics departments in the United States. In five of those departments women made up about 40 percent of the graduates, while in the other four departments women's representation among graduates was closer to the national average (about 20 percent at the time). The first group was defined as "successful," and the second group was defined as "typical." Whitten and her team wanted to know what set successful

---

[8]Barbara Whitten is a professor of physics at Colorado College. Her primary research is in the area of theoretical and computational atomic and molecular physics, and she has worked on problems in laser plasmas, Rydberg atoms, and low-energy electron collisions. She is also interested in gender and science, and for the past decade she has focused primarily on the experience of undergraduate women in physics. She has conducted research on what makes a physics department female-friendly in a project called What Works for Women in Physics?

departments apart from more typical departments. To answer this question, they gathered data from each department through interviews with faculty, students, administrators, and staff and observed courses and labs during two days in each department. The researchers found that the major difference between successful and typical departments was departmental culture (Whitten et al., 2003).

Similar to Margolis and Fisher, Whitten and her team found that many different factors help create a departmental culture and environment that are supportive and welcoming to female students. According to Whitten, most typical departments do some of these things, but successful departments do more of them, and they do them more consistently and more personally. Specifically, Whitten and her team found that the most successful departments supported activities and events that fostered a broader culture that was inclusive. Successful departments integrated students into the department soon after they declared a physics major and reached out to students taking introductory courses who might potentially major in physics. Successful departments often had a physics lounge and sponsored seminars, trips, and other social events. These activities provided opportunities for students to learn more about different applications of physics and career opportunities but also provided opportunities in which faculty and students could interact more informally to forge relationships.

Whitten was especially impressed with the model of historically black colleges and universities (HBCUs) for creating effective and supportive departmental cultures that help recruit and retain female science majors. HBCUs produce a disproportionate number of African American female physicists, and more than one-half of all African American physics degree holders, female and male at all levels, graduate from HBCUs (Whitten et al., 2004). Whitten says that HBCUs do many of the things that create a female-friendly department and do them exceptionally well. HBCUs support all their students, including women. As Whitten puts it, "You don't have to aim at women to have benefits for women."

HBCUs do one crucial thing that Whitten's team did not observe at other schools they visited in the first phase of the study: the schools provide a path toward a degree for students who do not come to college fully prepared to be physics majors. "Most schools don't recognize a category of student who would like to be a physics major, is interested in physics, and might be good at physics but who does not have the preparation straight from high school," Whitten told AAUW. The typical model is someone who has decided in high school that she or he wants to be a physics major and declares the major in college. HBCUs were the only schools that provided an alternative path to the major. Whitten believes that "if we could make a path like that in all schools, we would increase the diversity of physics majors." This is an example of how a department can change its approach to recruitment and increase diversity. Many students who do not have adequate high school preparation in physics can succeed at the college level if provided a path.

In the second phase of their research, Whitten and her team visited six physics departments at women's colleges and found that they and the HBCUs had a similar philosophy of student recruitment. Physics faculty at women's colleges know that few women come to college intending to major in physics, so active recruitment is a necessity. This reality forces faculty to think of "pathways rather than pipelines" and challenges the notion of a singular, linear route to becoming a physicist, which is more likely to reflect a white male experience (Whitten et al., 2007).

RECOMMENDATIONS

Whitten's research suggests that a female-friendly physics department should adopt all or some of the following practices:

- **Sponsor departmental social activities.**

  Seminars, lunches, and social events help integrate students into the department. Departments should also make an effort to invite potential majors to enroll in introductory courses and participate in social activities.

- **Provide a student lounge.**

  A lounge and other informal spaces in which undergraduate majors can interact outside of class can help integrate students and make the department feel more inclusive. Be sure that the lounge is welcoming and open to all students.

- **Actively recruit students into the major.**

  Provide interested and talented students who arrive at college underprepared or unsure that they want to study physics, or any other STEM subject, a pathway to the major. Offer introductory courses that appeal to students with different levels of physics preparation or background. The work of faculty at HBCUs to provide a pathway into physics for underprepared students is an excellent example of how critical this is to identifying and recruiting talented STEM students from more diverse backgrounds.

- **Sponsor a women-in-physics group.**

  In a male-dominated field like physics, having an informal group of female faculty and students can help female students. Groups like this can sponsor a variety of social and professional activities and, if possible, should be organized by a female faculty member as part of her departmental service, not as a volunteer activity.

Chapter 7.
University and College Faculty

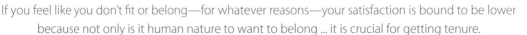

> If you feel like you don't fit or belong—for whatever reasons—your satisfaction is bound to be lower because not only is it human nature to want to belong ... it is crucial for getting tenure.
>
> —Cathy Trower[9]

Women's representation among faculty in STEM disciplines has increased over time, but women remain underrepresented among tenured faculty. In the fields of physics, engineering, and computer science, women are scarce at every level, so attracting and retaining female faculty is critical. For progress to occur in STEM fields, teachers and academic leaders must be selected from the entire pool of talented and qualified individuals; female faculty can also help recruit and retain female students and students from other underrepresented groups. Job satisfaction is a key to retention, but women and people of color are more likely than white men to report that they are less satisfied with the academic workplace, and, hence, women are more likely to leave the academy earlier in their career (Trower & Chait, 2002).

Cathy Trower is the research director of the Collaborative on Academic Careers in Higher Education (COACHE) at Harvard University. COACHE includes more than 130 colleges and universities that participate in the Tenure-Track Faculty Job Satisfaction Survey, which is administered annually to all full-time, tenure-track faculty at member institutions and asks about key components of faculty satisfaction. It asks junior faculty members to assess their experiences regarding promotion and tenure; the nature of their work; policies and practices; and the general climate, culture, and level of collegiality on their campuses. Trower and her colleagues found that female STEM faculty were less satisfied than their male colleagues with how well they "fit" in their departments, opportunities to work with senior faculty, and institutional support for having a family while on the tenure track.

Trower and Richard Chait founded COACHE in 2002 to help improve the academic environment for junior faculty and assist colleges and universities in recruiting, retaining, and increasing the satisfaction of early career faculty. Junior faculty are most at risk to leave academia during the early years, and their departure can incur both economic and cultural costs to institutions. Trower became interested in the topic of junior faculty satisfaction while she was working on a doctoral degree in higher education administration.

---

[9]Cathy Trower is a research associate at the Harvard University Graduate School of Education, where she heads the Collaborative on Academic Careers in Higher Education (COACHE). She has studied faculty employment issues, policy, and practices for 15 years, during which time she also produced an edited volume and numerous book chapters, articles, and case studies. She has made dozens of presentations on tenure policies and practices, faculty recruitment strategies, and issues facing women and minority faculty.

Although the data collected using the COACHE survey are not representative of all universities or colleges, they provide critical information about a current cohort of early career faculty. Additionally the data allow Trower and her colleagues to explore whether levels of satisfaction differ significantly by gender and academic discipline. Trower's findings on satisfaction among STEM faculty are described below. The data were collected from 1,809 STEM faculty members (587 women and 1,222 men) at 56 universities.

THE NATURE OF WORK AND DEPARTMENTAL CLIMATE

For both female and male STEM faculty, the nature of the work and the departmental climate were the most important factors predicting job satisfaction, and the two factors were equally important for both groups. Within the climate category, the researchers at COACHE identified 10 climate dimensions related to faculty satisfaction that are "actionable" by administrators (Trower, 2008):

- Fairness of evaluation by immediate supervisor
- Interest senior faculty take in your professional development
- Your opportunities to collaborate with senior colleagues
- Quality of **professional** interaction with **senior** colleagues
- Quality of **personal** interaction with **senior** colleagues
- Quality of **professional** interaction with **junior** colleagues
- Quality of **personal** interaction with **junior** colleagues
- How well you "fit" (i.e., your sense of belonging) in your department
- Intellectual vitality of the senior colleagues in your department
- Fairness of junior faculty treatment within your department

Female STEM faculty were less satisfied than their male peers were with all 10 factors and significantly less satisfied with three: sense of fit, opportunities to collaborate with senior colleagues, and the perception of fair treatment of junior faculty in one's department. The results of the COACHE survey show sense of fit to be the single most important climate factor predicting job satisfaction.

UNPACKING SENSE OF FIT

Trower defines "sense of fit" as one's sense of belonging in her or his department. In an interview with AAUW, she explained, "If you feel like you don't fit or belong—for whatever reasons—your satisfaction is bound to be lower, because not only is it human nature to want to belong ... it is crucial for getting tenure." She found that the sense of fit was enhanced for both women and men when they felt that they had good professional and personal interactions with colleagues, senior faculty had an interest in their professional development, and junior faculty were treated fairly.

Although good professional and personal interactions with colleagues are important for both female and male STEM faculty, such interactions may be critically important for women. Many STEM departments in various disciplines have only one or two women, so many female faculty may be the only women in their department. For example, most doctorate-granting geosciences institutions have only one woman per department (Holmes & O'Connell, 2003). More than one-half of all physics departments had only one or two women on their faculty in 2002, and only 20 physics departments had four or more female faculty (Ivie & Ray, 2005). "Because of the low numbers of women, isolation and lack of camaraderie/mentoring are particularly acute problems for women in fields such as engineering, physics, and computer science" (Rosser, 2004, p. xxii).

Isolation is a critical problem since it can be a major source of dissatisfaction among female faculty and can influence their decision to leave. Women report being excluded from informal social gatherings and more formal events, as well as from collaborating on research or teaching (Massachusetts Institute of Technology, 1999). Women are also less likely than their male colleagues to have role models or mentors and, therefore, get limited advice on navigating the workplace, professional and career development, and advancing in their careers (Macfarlane & Luzzadder-Beach, 1998; Rosser, 2004). A recent study by the National Academy of Sciences found that male faculty were significantly more likely than female faculty to report having discussions with colleagues about research, salary, and benefits. The study results also emphasized the importance of fit, highlighting that "the most problematic kind of attrition involves faculty who leave because they feel unwelcome. These faculty members have not failed but they also have not fit in, and the departments they leave have invested time, money and other resources that can be lost" (National Research Council, 2009, p. 98).

THE IMPORTANCE OF MENTORING

To promote a better sense of fit and belonging among faculty, Trower recommends that departments provide mentoring for all faculty. Mentoring helps address the feelings of isolation and marginalization that women in academic settings often report. Among STEM faculty in the COACHE survey, women rated the importance of formal mentoring significantly higher than men did. Trower told AAUW, "Mentoring is crucial for STEM women because without it they might not be privy to the good old boys' club or behind the scenes conversations that are crucial to fitting in the department and to getting tenure." Interestingly, women rated the importance of informal mentoring even higher than formal mentoring. Trower believes that this may be because "informal relationships arise organically, and because they are not part of a formal process, they may feel more natural, closer, more trusting and honest, which may be especially important to women in STEM, who are often in a numerical minority in their departments."

THE ROLE OF FAMILY RESPONSIBILITIES

The ability to balance work and family responsibilities also contributes to overall satisfaction, especially for STEM women in the COACHE sample. Overall, female faculty were less likely than male faculty to agree that their institutions supported having and raising a child while on the tenure track. Female STEM faculty were the least likely to agree with those sentiments and were significantly less satisfied than their male peers were with the balance between professional and personal time. Although difficulty trying to balance work and family responsibilities is not specific to women in STEM, Trower suggests that the nature of scientific research may make work-family balance particularly challenging for female STEM faculty: "The lab knows no official stop time—it's an unrelenting 24/7. It's difficult to just pack up and go home. Stopping for any period of time, to take advantage of stop-the-tenure-clock leave for instance, could be deadly to your research program." Although the effectiveness of work-life balance policies were significant predictors of women's satisfaction, both women and men in science and engineering fields found child care on their campuses lacking. Trower explains: "Child care is a huge issue everywhere I go. Most campuses do not offer adequate, if any, child care."

Women's representation among STEM faculty has increased significantly during the last four decades; however, women are still underrepresented in STEM fields and are more likely than men to work in lower faculty ranks. The findings from the COACHE survey indicate that both female and male faculty satisfaction are based on similar factors, including the nature of the work and departmental climate. Chilly departmental climates and isolation contribute to dissatisfaction among women, which can result in their departure from higher education. Family responsibilities and a department's work-life balance policies also have a greater influence on the satisfaction of female faculty compared with that of male faculty. This research suggests that if institutions improve the climate of their STEM departments as well as their work-life balance policies, they can better recruit and retain female faculty. Furthermore, because the factors that predict satisfaction are the same for female and male faculty in STEM, all faculty and institutions are likely to benefit from these improvements.

RECOMMENDATIONS

Trower recommends that departments focus on fit to improve faculty satisfaction and the experiences of female faculty in science and engineering disciplines:

- **Conduct departmental reviews to assess the climate for female faculty.**

  Although the climate within the department is important to both female and male faculty, it appears to be more important for female faculty and their overall satisfaction. When female faculty experience negative climates, they report lower job satisfaction and consider leaving their positions.

- **Create an environment that supports retention.**

  Ensure that new faculty are oriented to the university, school, and department. Cultivate an inclusive departmental culture by communicating consistent messages to all faculty, providing opportunities for junior faculty to collaborate with senior faculty, and ensuring the fair treatment of tenure-track faculty.

- **Ensure mentoring for all faculty.**

  Both formal and informal mentoring of junior faculty are important, and the latter is crucial to support the integration of women into science and engineering departments. Formal mentoring programs should be monitored and evaluated for effectiveness, and departments should foster informal mentoring by encouraging senior faculty to actively reach out to junior faculty.

- **Support faculty work-life balance.**

  Departments and universities should implement effective policies that support work-life balance. Stop-tenure-clock policies should allow both female and male faculty to stop their tenure clock for parental leave for anywhere from three months to a year after the birth or adoption of a child. These policies ensure that parents are not penalized for reduced productivity during the tenure-evaluation period. Providing on-site, high-quality child care also supports work-life balance and is important to female faculty satisfaction in particular.

Chapter 8.
Implicit Bias

> A widespread belief in American culture suggests that group membership should not constrain the choices and preferences of group members. Being a girl need not prevent one from becoming a police officer, senator, or mathematician. Being a boy need not prevent one from becoming a nurse, kindergarten teacher, or primary caregiver. In fact, all programs promoting equal opportunity seek the removal of external constraints for individual pursuits. Yet until the internal, mental constraints that link group identity with preference are removed, the patterns for self-imposed segregation may not change.
>
> — Brian Nosek, Mahzarin R. Banaji,[10] and Anthony Greenwald

Many people say they do not believe the stereotype that girls and women are not as good as boys and men in math and science. The research of Mahzarin Banaji, however, shows that even individuals who consciously refute gender and science stereotypes can still hold that belief at an unconscious level. These unconscious beliefs or implicit biases may be more powerful than explicitly held beliefs and values simply because we are not aware of them. Even if overt gender bias is waning, as some argue, research shows that less-conscious beliefs underlying negative stereotypes continue to influence assumptions about people and behavior.

Banaji is a professor of social ethics at Harvard University and a co-developer of the implicit association test (IAT) with Anthony Greenwald, professor of psychology at the University of Washington, and Brian Nosek, professor of psychology at the University of Virginia. Together they created and operate the Project Implicit website (https://implicit.harvard.edu), a virtual laboratory housing implicit association tests that measure the association between two concepts to determine attitudes about different social groups. For example, the gender-science IAT, which is the focus of this discussion, measures the association between math-arts and male-female (see figure 20).

For the gender-science IAT, participants (who take the test anonymously) complete two rounds of categorization. In each round, participants are asked to categorize 16 randomly ordered words, eight representing either "male" (for example, boy, son) or "female" (for example, daughter, girl) and eight representing either "science" (for example, physics, engineering) or "arts" (for example, English, history). In one round, participants use one key to indicate words representing male or science and another key to indicate words representing female or arts. In the second round the pairings are switched, and participants hit one response key to

---

[10]Mahzarin Banaji is the Richard Clarke Cabot Professor of Social Ethics and head tutor in the Department of Psychology at Harvard University. Her research focuses primarily on mental systems that operate in implicit or unconscious mode. With Brian Nosek and Anthony Greenwald, she maintains the educational website at https://implicit.harvard.edu, which was designed to create awareness about unconscious biases in self-professed egalitarians.

indicate if a word represents male or arts and another key if a word represents female or science.[11] The participants' response time for both rounds is measured, and the average response time when science is paired with male is compared with the average response time when science is paired with female.

**Figure 20. Instructions for an Implicit Association
Test on Gender and Science**

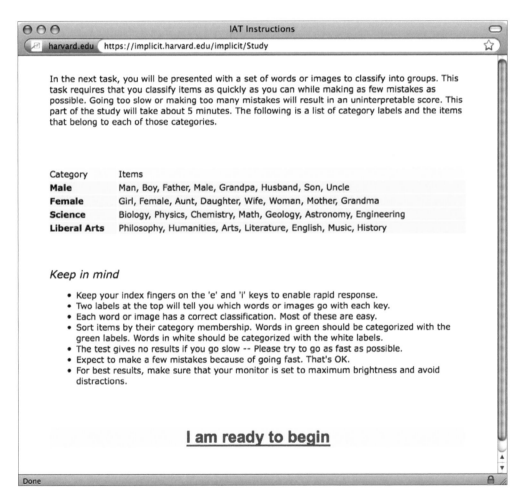

Source: Retrieved November 2009 from https://implicit.harvard.edu/implicit.

---

[11] The sequence of whether male is paired with science or arts first and female with the other is decided randomly for each test taker.

Since the gender-science test was established in 1998, more than a half million people from around the world have taken it, and more than 70 percent of test takers more readily associated "male" with science and "female" with arts than the reverse. This tendency is apparent in tests on the website and in the lab (Nosek et al., 2002a). These findings indicate a strong implicit association of male with science and female with arts and a high level of gender stereotyping at the unconscious level among both women and men of all races and ethnicities. The findings also challenge the notion that bias against women in math and science is a thing of the past.

Banaji did not begin her career in social psychology with an interest in gender bias. As a graduate student (supported by an AAUW fellowship) at Ohio State University, she studied social cognition, a broad field that looks at how people make decisions about other people and themselves. "I don't think that the word gender appeared even once in conversations in my five years in graduate school," Banaji remembers. In her first faculty position at Yale University, however, the results of a particular experiment caught her attention.

Jacoby et al. (1989) found that when individuals were shown random names, such as Sebastian Weisdorf, from a phone book, a few days later they were likely to identify that name as the name of a famous person from a list of both famous and unknown persons. Banaji explains: "Memory works in odd ways. Something that we have seen before lingers in our mind, and sometimes we use that information to incorrectly make decisions." She wondered if the same thing would happen with female names and replicated the experiment using the name Sally Weisdorf alongside Sebastian Weisdorf. Surprisingly, Banaji found that people were less likely to identify Sally as famous, even though both Sally and Sebastian were unknown. Women, it seemed, did not falsely "become famous" overnight like men. Based on this finding, Banaji concluded that people must unconsciously associate "male" and "fame" more readily than "female" and "fame." When asked if gender had anything to do with their choices, study participants said no, indicating that they were not conscious of their bias. This finding led Banaji to try to understand unconscious forms of bias. She told AAUW that these unconscious beliefs can help explain "how good people end up unintentionally making decisions that violate even their own sense of what's correct, what's good."

IMPLICIT BIASES AND GROUP IDENTIFICATION

In their first series of lab experiments to measure the strength of implicit attitudes between gender and math and science, Banaji and her colleagues worked with a sample of undergraduate students (40 women and 39 men) at Yale University. In one study, the researchers found that although both female and male participants had negative implicit attitudes toward math-science compared with language-arts, women showed a more negative evaluation of math-science (Nosek et al., 2002b). Additionally, women identified more strongly with arts than with math, but men showed no preference for either math or arts. Insofar as this result is representative of the population of the United States as a whole, Banaji says:

> The first effect is that our culture does not support the idea that studying math and science is a cool thing to do. That alone is something to worry about. However, girls and boys seem to know that if one or the other group is better at it, it's boys. When we look at how quickly men associate self with math, it's a lot more easily than do women. Often we hear from girls that it's not that they can't do math; it's that they don't identify with it. And that's critical—when you don't see yourself connected to a particular path, whether it is math-science or motherhood, the likelihood is that you will steer clear of it.

In the second study of another group of Yale undergraduates, Banaji and her colleagues measured the implicit math-gender stereotype and degree of gender identity. They found that both women and men held equally strong implicit stereotypes linking math to male. They also found that the degree to which female and male students identified with their gender group was related to their attitude toward math, math identity, and the endorsement of math-gender stereotypes (ibid.). For example, women who more closely identified with female identity showed more negative math attitudes and weaker math identity. According to Banaji, "The sad but clear implication of that result is that the more you associate with your group (female), the less you are likely to associate with math. Something has to give, so to speak, and it's not going to be the connection to your gender; math is psychologically more dispensable."

IMPLICIT GENDER-SCIENCE BIASES AND GENDER GAPS IN PERFORMANCE

Implicit gender-science biases may go beyond influencing individual behavior. The overall level of the implicit association of science with male in a country may be related to gender disparities in math and science performance. A recent study conducted by several researchers from several countries, including Banaji, examined whether national differences in implicit gender-science stereotypes could predict gender differences in performance in math and science.

The researchers hypothesized that a two-way relationship may exist between the level of gender-science stereotyping and gender differences in science performance. Stereotypes linking science with male may create gender differences in performance among students, and those gender differences in performance may reinforce the stereotypes linking science with male (Nosek et al., 2009). To test this idea the researchers examined whether a country's mean level of the implicit gender-science stereotype could predict gender difference in eighth grade performance in science on the Trends in International Mathematics and Science Study (TIMSS). Using data from almost 300,000 gender-science IATs completed by citizens of countries that participate in TIMSS, the researchers first determined the level of the implicit gender-science stereotype for each country by calculating the mean of all valid IAT scores for citizens from each country. Second, the researchers calculated the gender gap in performance by subtracting the average female performance from the average male performance for each of the 34 countries that took part in the 2003 TIMSS.

The results of the study showed a positive relationship between the implicit gender-science stereotype of the country and the gender difference in eighth grade science TIMSS performance. Specifically, the stronger the association between male and science in a country, the larger the male advantage in science performance. In this study, implicit biases predicted TIMSS performance better than self-reported stereotypes did. Because this study was correlational, the researchers could not determine whether the weaker performance of girls in science created the implicit gender-science stereotype or whether the stronger gender stereotype led to poorer female performance. Banaji believes, however, that it is the latter:

> The degree to which the idea that girls aren't good at science is in the air we breathe, the more likely it is to show up in patterns of attitudes, beliefs, and performance. If you look around you and only a fraction of those doing science come from group A, what are members of group A and B to think? It doesn't take too many neurons to figure out that perhaps group A isn't so good at science.

IMPLICIT BIAS AND WOMEN IN STEM

Overall, the implications of this research for women in science and engineering are significant. Implicit biases against women in science may prevent girls and women from pursuing science from the beginning, play a role in evaluations of girls' and women's course work in STEM subjects, influence parents' decisions to encourage or discourage their daughters from pursuing science and engineering careers, and influence employers' hiring decisions and evaluations of female employees.

Banaji points out that unconscious beliefs, once they are brought to the fore, can be changed if the holder of the belief so desires: "Implicit biases come from the culture. I think of them as the thumbprint of the culture on our minds. Human beings have the ability to learn to associate two things together very quickly—that is innate. What we teach ourselves, what we choose to associate is up to us."

RECOMMENDATION

- **Raise awareness of implicit bias.**

  A main purpose of the IAT is to help educate individuals about their implicit biases. Although implicit biases operate at an unconscious level and are influenced by our cultural environment, individuals can resolve to become more aware of how they make decisions and if and when their implicit biases may be at work in that process. Anyone can take the IAT at https://implicit.harvard.edu to gain a better understanding of their biases. Educators can look at the effect their biases have on their teaching, advising, and evaluation of students and can work to create an environment in the classroom that counters gender-science stereotypes. Parents can resolve to be more aware of messages they send their sons and daughters about their suitability for math and science.

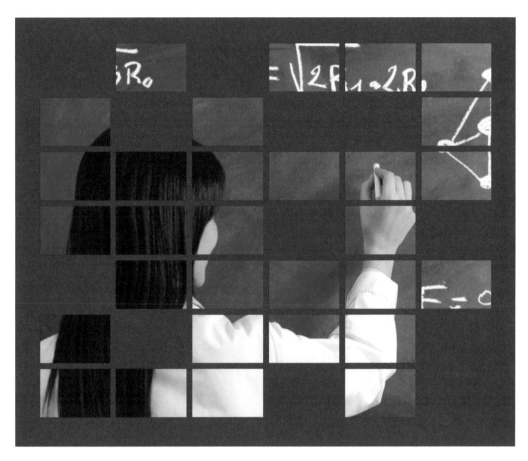

Chapter 9.
Workplace Bias

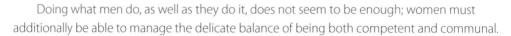

> Doing what men do, as well as they do it, does not seem to be enough; women must additionally be able to manage the delicate balance of being both competent and communal.
>
> — Madeline Heilman[12] and Tyler Okimoto

People tend to view women in "masculine" fields, such as most STEM fields, as either competent or likable but not both, according to Madeline Heilman, an organizational psychologist at New York University. In 2004 Heilman and her colleagues published the results of three experiments addressing the double bind facing women in masculine fields. The researchers found that when success in a male-type job was ambiguous, a woman was rated as less competent than an identically described man, although she was rated equally likable. When individuals working in a male-type job were clearly successful, however, women and men were rated as equally competent, but women were rated as less likable and more interpersonally hostile (for example, cold, pushy, conniving). This was not found to be true in fields that were "female" or gender-neutral. Heilman and her colleagues found that both competence and likability matter in terms of advancement, but women were judged to be less competent than men were in masculine fields unless there was clear evidence of excellence, and in that case, women were judged to be less likable—a classic double bind. In a follow-up study, Heilman and Okimoto (2007) found that successful women in masculine occupations are less likely to be disliked if they are seen as possessing communal traits such as being understanding, caring, and concerned about others.

Heilman's interest in examining how women in male-type fields can be penalized for their success was sparked when she co-authored an amicus brief to the U.S. Supreme Court in the case *Price Waterhouse v. Ann B. Hopkins* (American Psychological Association, 1991). Hopkins was a senior manager at Price Waterhouse when she was proposed for partnership in 1982. After review, her nomination was neither accepted nor rejected but was held for reconsideration the following year. When the partners in her office refused to propose her for partnership again the next year, she sued Price Waterhouse for sex discrimination. Hopkins was clearly competent. She had recently secured a $25 million contract with the U.S. Department of State, and the Supreme Court noted that the judge in her initial trial stated, "[N]one of the other partnership candidates at Price Waterhouse that year had a comparable record in terms of successfully securing major contracts for the partnership" (ibid, pp. 228, 234). Yet many of

---

[12]Madeline Heilman is a professor of psychology at New York University. Her research focuses on sex bias in work settings, the dynamics of stereotyping, and the unintended consequences of preferential selection processes. After receiving a doctorate from Columbia University, she spent eight years as a member of the faculty at the School of Organization and Management at Yale University. She serves on the boards of the *Journal of Applied Psychology* and *Academy of Management Review*.

the partners at Price Waterhouse clearly disliked Ann Hopkins. One partner described her as "macho," another suggested that she "overcompensated for being a woman," and a third advised her to take "a course at charm school." Several partners criticized her use of profanity, and the man who told Hopkins about the decision to place her candidacy on hold advised her to "walk more femininely, talk more femininely, dress more femininely, wear make-up, have her hair styled, and wear jewelry" (ibid., pp. 228, 234). The Hopkins case planted the seed for Heilman's research on penalties for success for women in male-type work.

THE DOUBLE BIND: BEING COMPETENT AND WELL LIKED

Although being both competent and well liked are important for advancement in the workplace, this balance may be more difficult for women than men to achieve in science and engineering fields. In the first of three experiments by Heilman and her colleagues, 48 undergraduates at a large northeastern university rated the competence and likability of three employees (one man, one woman, and one "dummy" man, whose information was held constant) in a male-type job: assistant vice president for sales in an aircraft company. The dummy man was included so it would not be obvious to participants that the purpose of the experiment was to examine differences in evaluation based on gender. Participant ratings of the dummy man were not part of the analysis. Participants were recruited from an introductory psychology course in which more than 90 percent of enrollees typically reported having work experience. The participants were given packets describing the responsibilities of the job, which included training and supervising junior executives, breaking into new markets, keeping abreast of industry trends, and generating new clients. The gender-type nature of the job was communicated via the products involved, including engine assemblies, fuel tanks, and other aircraft equipment and parts.

The students were split in half, and one group was told that the men and woman were about to undergo their annual performance review, so their performance was unclear. The other group was told that the men and woman were clearly successful and had recently been designated top performers by the organization. Participants rated female and male employees equally competent when the individual's prior success was made explicit. When information about performance was not provided, however, the woman was rated significantly less competent than the man. In terms of likability, participants were no more likely to choose the male than the female employee as more likable when performance was unclear, but when success was clear, participants overwhelmingly indicated that the man was more likable than the woman, with 19 of the 23 subjects choosing the successful man as more likable than the successful woman. Additionally, the woman was rated significantly more interpersonally

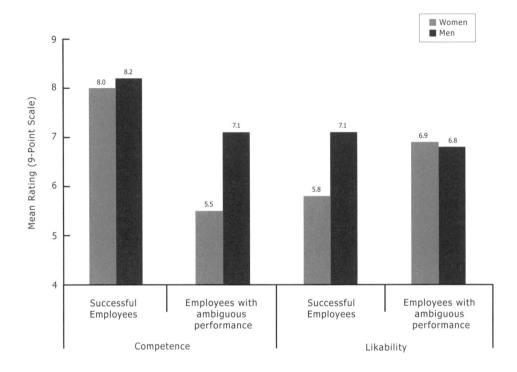

Figure 21. Competence and Likability for Women and Men in "Male" Professions

Mean Rating (9-Point Scale)

Women
Men

Competence:
- Successful Employees: Women 8.0, Men 8.2
- Employees with ambiguous performance: Women 5.5, Men 7.1

Likability:
- Successful Employees: Women 5.8, Men 7.1
- Employees with ambiguous performance: Women 6.9, Men 6.8

Source: Heilman et al., 2004, "Penalties for success: Reaction to women who succeed in male gender-typed tasks," *Journal of Applied Psychology, 89*(3), p. 420, Table 2.

hostile than the man when she was described as clearly successful, but the woman was rated significantly less interpersonally hostile than the man when performance was unclear (see figure 21).

In a second experiment 63 undergraduates at a large northeastern university rated the likability of successful women and men in male jobs, female jobs, and gender-neutral jobs. This time, the employee to be evaluated was the assistant vice president (AVP) of human resources; however, the division in which the employee was said to be working differed by gender type: the financial planning division (a male-type position), the employee assistance division (a female-type position), or the training division (a gender-neutral position). Participants were given packets describing the responsibilities of the jobs. The gender type of the positions was made clear through the job descriptions and responsibilities as well as by a section labeled "Characteristics of AVPs," which included the sex distribution of employees in the job

(86 percent male or female in the male- and female-type jobs, respectively, and 53 percent male in the neutral gender-type condition). The results of this study supported the results of the first study, indicating that successful women in male-type jobs are more likely to be disliked. The results also suggested that the negativity directed at successful women in male-type jobs does not extend to female-type or gender-neutral jobs.

In a third experiment designed to understand the career effects of being disliked, 131 participants made recommendations for salary increases and special career opportunities for female and male employees who were presented as more or less likable and more or less competent. This time, the experiment participants were full-time workers who were age 31, on average. Participants were provided a performance rating for an employee who had recently completed a yearlong management-training program. The rating included bar graphs indicating, on a scale from 0 to 10, the competence and likability of the individual as well as the average competence and likability of all 30 trainees. The participants evaluated the employee on a series of nine-point scales by answering questions such as, "Overall, how would you rate this individual?" (very low–very high); "How successful do you think this individual will be in this organization?" (not at all successful–very successful); and "How would you feel about working with this person as your manager?" (not pleased–pleased). Participants then answered the following questions related to special career opportunities on a nine-point scale from not at all to very much: "To what degree do you recommend placing this individual on the 'fast track'?" and "There are five highly prestigious upper-level positions available to the recent trainees. To what degree do you recommend this individual be placed in one of these five jobs?" Last, participants were asked to indicate which of five levels of potential salary they would recommend for the employee.

The results of this study indicated that likability and competence both matter for workplace success. Across the board, participants rated employees who were reported to be likable more favorably than those who were reported to be not likable. Competent employees were more highly recommended for special opportunities than were less competent employees, and likable employees, when competent, were more highly recommended for special opportunities than were less likable employees. Competent employees were recommended for a higher salary than were less competent employees, and likable employees, whether competent or not, were recommended for a higher salary than were less likable employees. These results suggest that being disliked can have detrimental effects in work settings. The most critical point from this research is that "whereas there are many things that lead an individual to be disliked, including obnoxious behavior, arrogance, stubbornness, and pettiness, it is only women, not men, for whom a unique propensity toward dislike is created by success in a nontraditional work situation" (Heilman et al., 2004, pp. 425–426). This suggests that success can create an additional impediment to women's upward mobility in male-dominated fields, even when they have done all the right things to move ahead in their careers.

In a follow-up study Heilman and Okimoto (2007) showed that the negativity directed at successful women in male occupations lessened when the women were viewed as "communal." For example, when told that a woman manager "is tough, yet understanding and concerned about others ... known to encourage cooperation and helpful behavior and has worked hard to increase her employees' sense of belonging," individuals no longer liked her less than a male counterpart and no longer preferred her male counterpart to her as a boss. If a woman was described as a mother, a role inferred to require communal traits, the negativity directed at her was eliminated as well, and the preference for men disappeared. Importantly, additional positive information that was not communal in nature, such as "outgoing and personable ... known to reward individual contributions," did not affect the negativity directed at successful women in male-type occupations; unless communal traits were ascribed to the women, participants consistently preferred men to women. These findings suggest that if women's success in male-type fields is accompanied by evidence of communality, negativity directed at these women can be averted. Heilman warns not to overinterpret this finding, however, and cautions that the bigger obstacle for most women in male-type work environments is being perceived as competent in the first place. If women emphasize their communal traits when it's not absolutely clear that they're competent, it might only feed into the notion that they're incompetent. The findings from the 2007 study suggest only that if a woman in a male-type field is clearly accepted as successful and competent, then emphasizing her communal qualities can temper some of the dislike typically directed at someone in her position.

IMPLICATIONS FOR FEMALE SCIENTISTS AND ENGINEERS

STEM fields are perceived as male, even fields like chemistry and math where almost one-half of degrees awarded now go to women.[13] Heilman's research shows how, in the absence of clear performance information, individuals view women in male-type occupations as less competent than men. When a woman has shown herself irrefutably to be competent in a male-type field, she then pays the price of social rejection in the form of being disliked. Being disliked appears to have clear consequences for evaluation and recommendations about reward allocation, including salary levels. Heilman's research may partially explain why women working in STEM occupations leave at higher rates than their male peers do: most people don't enjoy being assumed incompetent or, if thought competent, being disliked. This research may have

---

[13]The one exception is biology, which has started to shift away from being thought of as a male-type field.

implications for girls' aspirations for STEM careers as well, since the same disapproval directed at professional women who are successful at male-type tasks may be directed at girls who are successful at male-type tasks. In the words of Heilman and Okimoto (2007, p. 92), "Doing what men do, as well as they do it, does not seem to be enough; women must additionally be able to manage the delicate balance of being both competent and communal."

RECOMMENDATIONS

- **Raise awareness about bias against women in STEM fields.**

   If people are aware that gender bias exists in STEM fields, they can work to interrupt the unconscious thought processes that lead to bias. In particular, if women in science and engineering occupations are aware that gender bias exists in these fields, it may allow them to fortify themselves. When they encounter dislike from their peers, it may be helpful to know that they are not alone. Despite how it feels, the social disapproval is not personal, and women can counteract it.

- **Focus on competence.**

   Heilman's research shows that women may be disliked for being competent in traditionally male work roles. Nonetheless, Heilman encourages girls and women in STEM areas to focus on attaining competence in their work. Countering the social disapproval that may come from being perceived as competent is possible and preferable to being considered incompetent and never reaching higher-level positions.

- **Create clear criteria for success and transparency.**

   When the criteria for evaluation are vague or no objective measures of performance exist, an individual's performance is likely to be ambiguous, and when performance is ambiguous, people view women as less competent than men in STEM fields. Women and others facing bias are likely to do better in institutions with clear criteria for success and structures for evaluation. Transparency in the evaluation process is also important for anyone who may be subject to bias.

Chapter 10.
Recommendations

Why are so few women in science, technology, engineering, and mathematics? The answer lies in part in our perceptions and unconscious beliefs about gender in mathematics and science. Luckily, stereotypes, bias, and other cultural beliefs can change; often the very act of identifying a stereotype or bias begins the process of dismantling it. Following a review of the profiled case studies, AAUW offers recommendations in three areas: cultivating girls' achievement and interest in science and engineering, creating college environments that support women in science and engineering, and counteracting bias.

CULTIVATING GIRLS' ACHIEVEMENT AND INTEREST IN SCIENCE AND ENGINEERING

Parents and educators can do a great deal to encourage girls' achievement and interest in math and science. Unfortunately, the ancient and erroneous belief that boys are better equipped to tackle scientific and mathematical problems persists in many circles today, despite the tremendous progress that girls have made in science and math in recent decades. Research shows that negative stereotypes about girls' suitability for mathematical and scientific work are harmful in measurable ways. Even a subtle reference to gender stereotypes has been shown to adversely affect girls' math test performance. Stereotypes also influence girls' self-assessments in math, which influence their interest in pursuing science, technology, engineering, and mathematics careers. Fortunately, research also shows that actively countering stereotypes can lead to improvements in girls' performance and interest in math and science.

AAUW makes the following recommendations for cultivating girls' achievement and interest in science and engineering:

- **Spread the word about girls' and women's achievements in math and science.**

  The stereotype that men are better than women in STEM areas can affect girls' performance, how they judge their performance, and their aspirations. Help eliminate the stereotype by
    - exposing girls and boys to female role models in STEM careers,
    - talking about the greater numbers of girls and women who are achieving at higher levels in STEM subjects and fields than ever before, and
    - pointing out the lack of gender difference in performance in nearly every STEM subject.

  The more people hear this kind of information, the harder it becomes for them to believe that boys and men are better in these areas.

- **Teach girls that intellectual skills, including spatial skills, are acquired.**

  Teach girls that every time they work hard and learn something new, their brains form new connections, and over time they become smarter. Teach girls that passion, dedication, and self-improvement, not simply innate talent, are the road to achievement and contribution. Praise girls for their effort rather than their intelligence. Communicate to girls that seeking challenges, working hard, and learning from mistakes are valuable. These messages will teach girls the values that are at the heart of scientific and mathematical contributions: love of challenge, love of hard work, and the ability to embrace and learn from inevitable mistakes.

- **Teach students about stereotype threat and promote a growth-mindset environment.**

  Teaching students about stereotype threat can result in better performance for girls and young women, specifically on high-stakes tests. Additionally, girls in a growth-mindset environment are less affected by stereotype threat in science and math. Create a growth-mindset environment in the classroom by emphasizing that intellectual skills can be improved with effort and perseverance and that anyone who works hard can succeed.

- **Talented and gifted programs should send the message that they value growth and learning.**

  Talented and gifted programs can benefit students by sending the message that students are in these programs not because they have been bestowed with a "gift" of great ability but because they are advanced in certain areas and the program will help them further develop their abilities. Consider changing the name of talented and gifted programs to "challenge" or "advanced" programs to emphasize more of a growth mindset and less of a fixed mindset.

- **Encourage children to develop their spatial skills.**

  Encourage children to play with construction toys, take things apart and put them back together again, play games that involve fitting objects into different places, draw, and work with their hands. Spatial skills developed in elementary and middle school can promote student interest in mathematics, physics, and other areas. Girls and boys with good spatial skills may be more confident about their abilities and express greater interest in pursuing certain STEM subjects and learning about careers in engineering.

- **Help girls recognize their career-relevant skills.**

  Girls are less likely than boys to interpret their academic successes in math and science as an indication that they have the skills necessary to become a successful engineer, physicist, or computer scientist. Encourage girls to see their success in high school math and science for what it is: not just a requirement for going to college but also an indication that they have the skills to succeed in a whole range of science and engineering professions.

- **Encourage high school girls to take calculus, physics, chemistry, computer science, and engineering classes when available.**

  Girls who take calculus in high school are three times more likely than girls who do not to major in a scientific or engineering field in college. Taking higher-level science and math classes in high school keeps career options open.

- **Make performance standards and expectations clear.**

  The same letter or number grade on an assignment or exam might signal something different to girls than it does to boys. Educators can help students understand their grades by using phrases such as, "If you got above an 80 on this test, you are doing a great job in this class." The more educators can reduce uncertainty about students' performance, the less students will fall back on stereotypes to assess themselves.

CREATING COLLEGE ENVIRONMENTS THAT SUPPORT WOMEN IN SCIENCE AND ENGINEERING

Although many young women graduate from high school well prepared to pursue a science or engineering major, relatively few women pursue majors in science, technology, engineering, or mathematics, and when they do, many capable women leave these majors before graduation. Even fewer women are present on science and engineering faculty. Research finds that small improvements in the culture of a department can have a positive effect on the recruitment and retention of female students. Likewise, departments that work to integrate female faculty and enhance a sense of community are also more likely to recruit and retain female faculty.

AAUW makes the following recommendations for creating college environments that support women in science and engineering:

To attract and retain more female students

- **Actively recruit women into STEM majors.**

  Qualified women are less likely to have considered science and engineering majors than are their male peers. Colleges and universities should reach out to high school girls to inform them about the science and engineering majors that they offer. For women who arrive at college underprepared or unsure of what they want to study, provide a pathway to major in a STEM field. Offer introductory courses that appeal to students with different levels of preparation or background in the major. These measures can be critical for identifying and recruiting talented STEM students from diverse backgrounds.

- **Send an inclusive message about who makes a good science or engineering student.**

  Admissions policies that require experience that will be taught in the curriculum (for example, requiring computer science major applicants to have significant prior computer programming experience) may weed out potentially successful students, especially women. Revising admissions policies to send a more inclusive message about who can be successful in STEM majors can help departments recruit more qualified, capable women.

- **Emphasize real-life applications in early STEM courses.**

  Presenting the broad applications of science and engineering to students early in their college career builds students' interest and confidence. Early college courses emphasizing real-world applications of STEM work have been shown to increase the retention of women in STEM majors.

- **Teach professors about stereotype threat and the benefits of a growth mindset.**

  Research shows that professors can reduce stereotype threat in their classrooms and change students' mindsets from fixed to growth through the messages they send their students. Educate professors about stereotype threat, the benefits of a growth mindset, and how to create a growth-mindset environment in their classrooms by sending students the message that intellectual skills can be acquired and anyone who works hard can succeed.

- **Make performance standards and expectations clear in STEM courses.**

  Extremely low average test scores are common in many college science and engineering courses. Low scores increase uncertainty in all students, but they have a more negative effect on students who already feel like they don't belong, as many women in STEM majors do. Clarifying what is expected can help students more accurately judge their performance. The more professors can reduce uncertainty about students' performance, the less students will fall back on stereotypes to assess themselves.

- **Take proactive steps to support women in STEM majors.**

  - Sponsor seminars, lunches, and social events to help integrate women into the department.
  - Ensure that no student clique dominates or becomes the ideal way of "being" in a STEM major.
  - Provide a welcoming student lounge open to all students to encourage interaction outside of class.
  - Sponsor a "women in (STEM major)" group.

- **Enforce Title IX in science, technology, engineering, and math.**

  Title IX is an important tool to help create equal opportunities and full access to STEM fields for women. Title IX compliance reviews by federal agencies ensure gender equity in STEM education.

To attract and retain female faculty

- **Conduct departmental reviews to assess the climate for female faculty.**

  Although the climate within the department is important to both female and male faculty, it appears to be more important for female faculty and their overall satisfaction. When female faculty experience a negative climate, they report lower job satisfaction and are more likely to consider leaving their position.

- **Ensure mentoring for all faculty.**

  Both formal and informal mentoring of junior faculty are important, and the latter is crucial to support the integration of women into science and engineering departments.

- Support faculty work-life balance.

  Policies that effectively support work-life balance such as stop-tenure-clock policies and on-site, high-quality child care are especially important to female faculty
  satisfaction.

COUNTERACTING BIAS

Bias against women—both implicit and explicit—still exists in science and engineering. Even
individuals who actively reject gender stereotypes often hold unconscious biases about women
in scientific and engineering fields. Women in "male" jobs like engineering can also face overt
discrimination.

AAUW makes the following recommendations for counteracting bias:

- Learn about your own implicit bias.

  Take the implicit association tests at https://implicit.harvard.edu to gain a better
  understanding of your own biases.

- Keep your biases in mind.

  Although implicit biases operate at an unconscious level, individuals can resolve
  to become more aware of how they make decisions and if and when their implicit
  biases may be at work in that process.

- Take steps to correct for your biases.

  Educators can look at the influence their biases have on their teaching, advising, and
  evaluation of students and can work to create an environment in the classroom that
  counters gender-science stereotypes. Parents can resolve to be more aware of messages they send their sons and daughters about their suitability for math and science.

- Raise awareness about bias against women in STEM fields.

  If scientists and engineers are aware that gender bias is a reality in STEM fields,
  they can work to interrupt the unconscious thought processes that lead to bias.
  If women in particular in science and engineering occupations are aware that
  gender bias exists in these fields, it may allow them to fortify themselves. When
  they encounter dislike from their peers, it may be helpful to know that they are not
  alone. Despite how it feels, the social disapproval is not personal, and women can
  counteract it.

- Create clear criteria for success and transparency.

  When the criteria for evaluation are vague or no objective measures of performance exist, an individual's performance is likely to be ambiguous. When performance is ambiguous, people view women in STEM fields as less competent than men in those fields. Women and others facing bias are likely to do better in institutions with clear criteria for success, clear structures for evaluation, and transparency in the evaluation process.

Bibliography

AAUW. (2008). *Where the girls are: The facts about gender equity in education*, by C. Corbett, C. Hill, & A. St. Rose. Washington, DC: Author.

AAUW Educational Foundation. (2007). *Behind the pay gap*, by J. G. Dey & C. Hill. Washington, DC: Author.

Ambady, N., Shih, M., Kim, A., & Pittinsky, T. (2001, September). Stereotype susceptibility in children: Effects of identity activation on quantitative performance. *Psychological Science, 12*(5), 385–90.

American Psychological Association. (1991). In the Supreme Court of the United States: *Price Waterhouse v. Ann B. Hopkins*: Amiens curiae brief for the American Psychological Association. *American Psychologist, 46*, 1061–70.

American Society for Quality. (2009). *Engineering image problem could fuel shortage.* Milwaukee, WI: Author. Retrieved December 23, 2009, from www.asq.org/media-room/press-releases/2009/20090122-engineering-image.html.

Andreescu, T., Gallian, J. A., Kane, J. M., & Mertz, J. E. (2008). Cross-cultural analysis of students with exceptional talent in mathematical problem solving. *Notices of the American Mathematical Society, 55*(10), 1248–60.

Aronson, J., Fried, C. B., & Good, C. (2002). Reducing the effects of stereotype threat on African American college students by shaping theories of intelligence. *Journal of Experimental Social Psychology, 38*(2), 113–25.

Baenninger, M., & Newcombe, N. (1989). The role of experience in spatial test performance: A meta-analysis. *Sex Roles, 20*(5-6), 327–44.

Benbow, C. P., & Stanley, J. C. (1983). Sex differences in mathematical reasoning ability: More facts. *Science, 222*, 1029–31.

Bentley, J. T., & Adamson, R. (2003). *Gender differences in the careers of academic scientists and engineers: A literature review* (NSF 03-322). Arlington, VA: National Science Foundation.

Blackwell, L. S., Trzesniewski, K. H., & Dweck, C. S. (2007). Implicit theories of intelligence predict achievement across an adolescent transition: A longitudinal study and an intervention. *Child Development, 78*(1), 246–63.

Blascovich, J., Spencer, S. J., Quinn, D., & Steele, C. (2001). African-Americans and high blood pressure: The role of stereotype threat. *Psychological Science, 12*(3), 225–29.

Brainard, S. G., & Carlin, L. (1998). A six-year longitudinal study of undergraduate women in engineering and science. *Journal of Engineering Education, 87*(4), 369–75.

Brody, L. E., & Mills, C. J. (2005). Talent search research: What have we learned? *High Ability Studies, 16*(1), 97–111.

Buck, G. A., Plano Clark, V. L., Leslie-Pelecky, D., Lu, Y., & Cerda-Lizarraga, P. (2008). Examining the cognitive processes used by adolescent girls and women scientists in identifying science role models: A feminist approach. *Science Education, 92*(4), 688–707.

Ceci, S. J., Williams, W. M., & Barnett, S. M. (2009). Women's underrepresentation in science: Sociocultural and biological considerations. *Psychological Bulletin, 135*(2), 218–61.

Cohoon, J. M., & Aspray, W. (2006). A critical review of the research on women's participation in postsecondary computing education. In J. M. Cohoon & W. Aspray (Eds.), *Women and information technology: Research on under-representation* (pp. 137–79). Cambridge, MA: MIT Press.

Cooper, S. E., & Robinson, D. A. G. (1991). The relationship of mathematics self-efficacy beliefs to mathematics anxiety and performance. *Measurement and Evaluation in Counseling and Development, 24*(1), 4–11.

Correll, S. J. (2001). Gender and the career choice process: The role of biased self-assessments. *American Journal of Sociology, 106*(6), 1691–1730.

———. (2004). Constraints into preferences: Gender, status, and emerging career aspirations. *American Sociological Review, 69*(1), 93–113.

Diekman, A. B., Brown, E. R., Johnston, A. M., & Clark, E. K. (2009, June). *Communal goals as inhibitors of STEM careers*. Poster presented at the National Science Foundation Joint Annual Meeting, Washington, DC.

Di Fabio, N. M., Brandi, C., & Frehill, L. M. (2008). *Professional women and minorities: A total human resources data compendium*. Washington, DC: Commission on Professionals in Science and Technology.

Dweck, C. (2006). Is math a gift? Beliefs that put females at risk. In S. J. Ceci & W. M. Williams (Eds.), *Why aren't more women in science? Top researchers debate the evidence* (pp. 47–55). Washington, DC: American Psychological Association.

———. (2008). *Mindsets and math/science achievement.* New York: Carnegie Corporation of New York, Institute for Advanced Study, Commission on Mathematics and Science Education.

Dweck, C., & Leggett, E. L. (1988). A social-cognitive approach to motivation and personality. *Psychological Review, 95*(2), 256–73.

Eccles, J. S. (1994). Understanding women's educational and occupational choices: Applying the Eccles et al. model of achievement-related choices. *Psychology of Women Quarterly, 18*(4), 585–609.

———. (2006). Where are all the women? Gender differences in participation in physical science and engineering. In S. J. Ceci & W. M. Williams (Eds.), *Why aren't more women in science? Top researchers debate the evidence* (pp. 199–210). Washington, DC: American Psychological Association.

Eccles (Parsons), J. S., Adler, T. F., Futterman, R., Goff, S. B., Kaczala, C. M., Meece, J. L., & Midgley, C. (1983). Expectancies, values, and academic behaviors. In J. T. Spence (Ed.), *Perspective on achievement and achievement motivation* (pp. 75–146). San Francisco: W. H. Freeman.

Eisenhart, M. (2008, October). *We can't get there from here: High school girls consider engineering.* Presentation for a Women in Engineering ProActive Network (WEPAN) national webcast.

Farenga, S. J., & Joyce, B. A. (1999). Intentions of young students to enroll in science courses in the future: An examination of gender differences. *Science Education, 83*(1), 55–76.

Foschi, M. (1996). Double standards in the evaluation of men and women. *Social Psychology Quarterly, 59*(3), 237–54.

Fouad, N. A., & Walker, C. M. (2005). Cultural influences on responses to items on the Strong Interest Inventory. *Journal of Vocational Behavior, 66*(1), 104–23.

Frehill, L. M., Brandi, C., Di Fabio, N., Keegan, K., & Hill, S. T. (2009, Summer). Women in engineering: A review of the 2008 literature. *SWE Magazine, 55*, 28–56.

Frehill, L. M., Di Fabio, N., Hill, S., Trager, K., & Buono, J. (2008, Summer). Women in engineering: A review of the 2007 literature. *SWE Magazine, 54*(3), 6–30.

Frizell, S., & Nave, F. (2008). *A preliminary analysis of factors affecting the persistence of African-American females in engineering degree programs.* Paper presented at the American Society for Engineering Education Annual Conference, Pittsburgh, PA.

Gibbons, M. T. (2009, June). Engineering by the numbers. In *Profiles of engineering and engineering technology colleges.* Washington, DC: American Society for Engineering Education.

Ginther, D. K., & Kahn, S. (2006). *Does science promote women? Evidence from academia 1973–2001* (NBER Working Paper W12691). Cambridge, MA: National Bureau of Economic Research.

Good, C., Aronson, J., & Harder, J. A. (2008). Problems in the pipeline: Stereotype threat and women's achievement in high-level math courses. *Journal of Applied Developmental Psychology, 29*(1), 17–28.

Good, C., Aronson, J., & Inzlicht, M. (2003). Improving adolescents' standardized test performance: An intervention to reduce the effects of stereotype threat. *Applied Developmental Psychology, 24*, 645–62.

Good, C., Rattan, A., & Dweck, C. S. (2009). Why do women opt out? Sense of belonging and women's representation in mathematics. Unpublished paper, Baruch College, Stanford University.

Goulden, M., Frasch, K., & Mason, M. A. (2009). *Staying competitive: Patching America's leaky pipeline in the sciences.* Berkeley: University of California, Berkeley Center on Health, Economic, & Family Security, & The Center for American Progress.

Grant, H., & Dweck, C. S. (2003). Clarifying achievement goals and their impact. *Journal of Personality and Social Psychology, 85*(3), 541–53.

Guay, R. (1977). *Purdue Spatial Visualization Test: Rotations.* West Lafayette, IN: Purdue Research Foundation.

Guiso, L., Monte, F., Sapienza, P., & Zingales, L. (2008, May 30). Culture, gender, and math. *Science, 320,* 1164–65.

Haier, R. J., Jung, R. E., Yeo, R. A., Head, K., & Alkire, M. T. (2005). The neuroanatomy of general intelligence: Sex matters. *NeuroImage, 25,* 320–27.

Halpern, D. F., Aronson, J., Reimer, N., Simpkins, S., Star, J. R., & Wentzel, K. (2007). *Encouraging girls in math and science* (NCER 2007-2003). Washington, DC: U.S. Department of Education, National Center for Education Research.

Halpern, D. F., Benbow, C. P., Geary, D. C., Gur, R. C., Hyde, J. S., & Gernsbacher, M. A. (2007). The science of sex differences in science and mathematics. *Psychological Science in the Public Interest, 8*(1), 1–51.

Hanson, S. L. (2004). African American women in science: Experiences from high school through the post-secondary years and beyond. *NWSA Journal, 16*(1), 96–115.

Hartung, P. J., Porfeli, E. J., & Vondracek, F. W. (2005). Child vocational development: A review and reconsideration. *Journal of Vocational Behavior, 66*(3), 385–419.

Hedges, L. V., & Nowell, A. (1995, July 7). Sex differences in mental test scores, variability, and numbers of high-scoring individuals. *Science, 269,* 41–45.

Heilman, M. E., & Okimoto, T. G. (2007). Why are women penalized for success at male tasks? The implied communality deficit. *Journal of Applied Psychology, 92*(1), 81–92.

Heilman, M. E., Wallen, A. S., Fuchs, D., & Tamkins, M. M. (2004). Penalties for success: Reaction to women who succeed in male gender-typed tasks. *Journal of Applied Psychology, 89*(3), 416–27.

Hewlett, S. A., Buck Luce, C., Servon, L. J., Sherbin, L., Shiller, P., Sosnovich, E., & Sumberg, K. (2008). *The Athena Factor: Reversing the brain drain in science, engineering and technology* (Harvard Business Review Research Report). Boston: Harvard Business Publishing.

Higher Education Research Institute. (2007, January). *Survey of the American freshman: Special tabulations.* Los Angeles, CA: Author.

Holmes, M. A., & O'Connell, S. (2003). *Where are the women geoscience professors?* Paper presented at the National Science Foundation, Association for Women Geoscientists, and Association for Women Geoscientists Foundation-sponsored workshop, Washington, DC.

Hyde, J. S., Lindberg, S. M., Linn, M. C., Ellis, A. B., & Williams, C. C. (2008, July 25). Gender similarities characterize math performance. *Science, 321,* 494–95.

Inzlicht, M., & Ben-Zeev, T. (2000). A threatening intellectual environment: Why females are susceptible to experiencing problem-solving deficits in the presence of males. *Psychological Science, 11*(5), 365–71.

Ivie, R., & Ray, K. N. (2005). *Women in physics and astronomy, 2005* (AIP Publication Number R-430.02). College Park, MD: American Institute of Physics.

Jacoby, L. L., Kelley, C., Brown, J., & Jasechko, J. (1989). Becoming famous overnight: Limits on the ability to avoid unconscious influences of the past. *Journal of Personality and Social Psychology, 56*, 326–38.

Johns, M., Schmader, T., & Martens, A. (2005). Knowing is half the battle: Teaching stereotype threat as a means of improving women's math performance. *Psychological Science, 16*(3), 175–79.

Jozefowicz, D. M., Barber, B. L., & Eccles, J. S. (1993, March 28). *Adolescent work-related values and beliefs: Gender differences and relation to occupational aspirations.* Paper presented at the Biennial Meeting of the Society for Research on Child Development, New Orleans, LA.

Kimura, D. (2002). Sex hormones influence human cognitive pattern. *Neuroendocrinology Letters, 23*(Suppl. 4), 67–77.

Konrad, A. M., Ritchie, J. E., Jr., Lieb, P., & Corrigall, E. (2000). Sex differences and similarities in job attribute preferences: A meta-analysis. *Psychological Bulletin, 126*(4), 593–641.

Kulis, S., Sicotte, D., & Collins, S. (2002). More than a pipeline problem: Labor supply constraints and gender stratification across academic science disciplines. *Research in Higher Education, 43*(6), 657–91.

Lacey, T. A., & Wright, B. (2009, November). Occupational employment projections to 2018. *Monthly Labor Review, 132*(11), 82–123.

Lapan, R. T., Adams, A., Turner, S., & Hinkelman, J. M. (2000). Seventh graders' vocational interest and efficacy expectation patterns. *Journal of Career Development, 26*(3), 215–29.

Lent, R. W., Brown, S. D., & Larkin, K. C. (1986). Self-efficacy in the prediction of academic performance and perceived career options. *Journal of Counseling Psychology, 33*(3), 265–69.

Linn, M. C., & Petersen, A. C. (1985). Emergence and characterization of sex differences in spatial ability: A meta-analysis. *Child Development, 56*(6), 1479–98.

Lovaglia, M. J., Lucas, J. W., Houser, J. A., Thye, S. R., & Markovsky, B. (1998). Status processes and mental ability test scores. *American Journal of Sociology, 104*(1), 195–228.

Low, K. S. D., Yoon, M., Roberts, B. W., & Rounds, J. (2005). The stability of vocational interests from early adolescence to middle adulthood: A quantitative review of longitudinal studies. *Psychological Bulletin, 131*(5), 713–37.

Lubinski, D., & Benbow, C. P. (1992). Gender differences in abilities and preferences among the gifted: Implications for the math-science pipeline. *Current Directions in Psychological Science, 1*(2), 61–66.

———. (2006). Study of mathematically precocious youth after 35 years: Uncovering antecedents for the development of math-science expertise. *Perspectives on Psychological Science, 1*(4), 316–45.

Lynn, R., & Irwing, P. (2004). Sex differences on the Progressive Matrices: A meta-analysis. *Intelligence, 32*(5), 481–98.

Macfarlane, A., & Luzzadder-Beach, S. (1998). Achieving equity between women and men in the geosciences. *Geological Society of America Bulletin, 110*(12), 1590–1614.

Margolis, J., & Fisher, A. (2002). *Unlocking the clubhouse: Women in computing.* Cambridge: Massachusetts Institute of Technology.

Margolis, J., Fisher, A., & Miller, F. (2002). *Caring about connections: Gender and computing.* Pittsburgh, PA: Carnegie Mellon University, School of Computer Science.

Mason, M. A., & Goulden, M. (2002, November-December). Do babies matter? The effect of family formation on the lifelong careers of academic men and women. *Academe, 88*(6), 21–27.

———. (2004). Marriage and baby blues: Redefining gender equity in the academy. *Annals of the American Academy of Political and Social Science, 596*(1), 86–103.

Mason, M. A., Goulden, M., & Frasch, K. (2009, January-February). Why graduate students reject the fast track. *Academe Online, 95*(1).

Massachusetts Institute of Technology. School of Science. Committee on Women Faculty. (1999). *A study of the status of women faculty in science at MIT.* Cambridge, MA.

May, G. S., & Chubin, D. E. (2003). A retrospective on undergraduate engineering success for underrepresented minority students. *Journal of Engineering Education, 92*(1), 27–40.

McIntyre, R. B., Lord, C. G., Gresky, D. M., Ten Eyck, L. L., Frye, G. D. J., & Bond, C. F., Jr. (2005). A social impact trend in the effects of role models on alleviating women's mathematics stereotype threat. *Current Research in Social Psychology, 10*(9), 116–36.

McIntyre, R. B., Paulson, R. M., & Lord, C. G. (2003). Alleviating women's mathematics stereotype threat through salience of group achievements. *Journal of Experimental Social Psychology, 39*(1), 83–90.

Munro, N. (2009, July 4). Science faces Title IX test. *National Journal Magazine.*

National Academy of Engineering. Committee on Public Understanding of Engineering Messages. (2008). *Changing the conversation: Messages for improving public understanding of engineering.* Washington, DC: National Academies Press.

National Academy of Sciences. (2007). *Beyond bias and barriers: Fulfilling the potential of women in academic science and engineering.* Washington, DC: National Academies Press.

National Academy of Sciences. Committee on Science, Engineering & Public Policy. (2007). *Rising above the gathering storm: Energizing and employing America for a brighter economic future.* Washington, DC: National Academies Press.

National Association of Colleges and Employers. (2009, Fall). Salary survey.

National Research Council. (2009). *Gender differences at critical transitions in the careers of science, engineering and mathematics faculty.* Washington, DC: National Academies Press.

National Research Council. Committee on Support for Thinking Spatially. (2006). *Learning to think spatially: GIS as a support system in the K-12 curriculum.* Washington, DC: National Academies Press.

National Science Board. (2008). *Science and engineering indicators 2008* (Volume 1, NSB 08-01; Volume 2, NSB 08-01A). Arlington, VA: National Science Foundation.

———. (2010). *Science and engineering indicators 2010* (NSB 10-01). Arlington, VA: National Science Foundation.

National Science Foundation. Division of Science Resources Statistics. (2008). *Science and engineering degrees: 1966–2006* (Detailed Statistical Tables) (NSF 08-321). Arlington, VA: Author. Retrieved December 22, 2009, from www.nsf.gov/statistics/nsf08321/pdf/nsf08321.pdf.

———. (2009a). *Characteristics of doctoral scientists and engineers in the United States: 2006* (Detailed Statistical Tables) (NSF 09-317). Arlington, VA: Author.

———. (2009b). *Women, minorities, and persons with disabilities in science and engineering: 2009* (NSF 09-305). Arlington, VA: Author. Retrieved December 22, 2009, from www.nsf.gov/statistics/wmpd.

Nelson, D. J., & Rogers, C. (n.d.). *A national analysis of diversity in science and engineering faculties at research universities.* Retrieved October 24, 2009, from www.now.org/issues/diverse/diversity_report.pdf.

Nguyen, H.-H. H., & Ryan, A. M. M. (2008). Does stereotype threat affect test performance of minorities and women? A meta-analysis of experimental evidence. *Journal of Applied Psychology, 93*(6), 1314–34.

Nosek, B. A., Banaji, M. R., & Greenwald, A. G. (2002a). Harvesting implicit group attitudes and beliefs from a demonstration web site. *Group Dynamics: Theory, Research, and Practice, 6*(1), 101–15.

———. (2002b). Math = male, me = female, therefore math ≠ me. *Journal of Personality and Social Psychology, 83*(1), 44–59.

Nosek, B. A., Smyth, F. L., Sriram, N., Lindner, N. M., Devos, T., Ayala, A., & Bar-Anan, Y. (2009). National differences in gender-science stereotypes predict national sex differences in science and math achievement. *Proceedings of the National Academy of Science, 106*(26), 10593–97.

Ohland, M. W., Sheppard, S. D., Lichtenstein, G., Eris, O., Chachra, D., & Layton, R. A. (2008). Persistence, engagement, and migration in engineering programs. *Journal of Engineering Education, 97*(3), 259–78.

Pajares, F. (1996). Self-efficacy beliefs and mathematical problem-solving of gifted students. *Contemporary Educational Psychology, 21*(4), 325–44.

———. (2005). Gender differences in mathematics self-efficacy beliefs. In A. M. Gallagher & J. C. Kaufman (Eds.), *Gender differences in mathematics: An integrative psychological approach* (pp. 294–315). Boston: Cambridge University Press.

Paulsen, C. A., & Bransfield, C. P. (2009). *"Engineer Your Life" evaluation report for year 2.* Concord, MA: Veridian InSight LLC.

Perna, L., Lundy-Wagner, V., Drezner, N. D., Gasman, M., Yoon, S., Bose, E., & Gary, S. (2009). The contribution of HBCUs to the preparation of African American women for STEM careers: A case study. *Research in Higher Education, 50*(1), 1–23.

Pieronek, C. (2005). Title IX and gender equity in science, technology, engineering and mathematics education: No longer an overlooked application of the law. *Journal of College and University Law, 31*(2), 291–350.

———. (2009). *Federal Title IX reviews: What they really mean.* Paper presented at the American Society for Engineering Education Annual Conference, Austin, TX.

Plant, E. A., Baylor, A. L., Doerr, C. E., & Rosenberg-Kima, R. B. (2009). Changing middle-school students' attitudes and performance regarding engineering with computer-based social models. *Computers and Education, 53*(2), 209–15.

Rosser, S. V. (2004). *The science glass ceiling: Academic women scientists and the struggle to succeed.* New York: Routledge.

Sax, L. J. (1994). Retaining tomorrow's scientists: Exploring the factors that keep male and female college students interested in science careers. *Journal of Women and Minorities in Science and Engineering, 1*(1), 45–61.

Seymour, E., & Hewitt, N. M. (1997). *Talking about leaving: Why undergraduates leave the sciences.* Boulder, CO: Westview Press.

Simard, C., Henderson, A. D., Gilmartin, S. K., Schiebinger, L., & Whitney, T. (2008). *Climbing the technical ladder: Obstacles and solutions for mid-level women in technology.* Stanford, CA: Michelle R. Clayman Institute for Gender Research, Stanford University, & Anita Borg Institute for Women and Technology.

Singh, K., Allen, K. R., Scheckler, R., & Darlington, L. (2007). Women in computer-related majors: A critical synthesis of research and theory from 1994–2005. *Review of Educational Research, 77*(4), 500–33.

Society of Women Engineers. (2006). Attitudes and experiences of engineering alumni, by Harris Interactive. Unpublished PowerPoint presentation.

Sorby, S. A. (2009). Educational research in developing 3-D spatial skills for engineering students. *International Journal of Science Education, 31*(3), 459–80.

Sorby, S. A., & Baartmans, B. J. (2000). The development and assessment of a course for enhancing the 3-D spatial visualization skills of first year engineering students. *Journal of Engineering Education, 89*(3), 301–07.

Spencer, S. J., Steele, C. M., & Quinn, D. M. (1999). Stereotype threat and women's math performance. *Journal of Experimental Social Psychology, 35*(1), 4–28.

Stack, S. (2004). Gender, children and research productivity. *Research in Higher Education, 45*(8), 891–920.

Steele, C. M. (1997). A threat in the air: How stereotypes shape intellectual identity and performance. *American Psychologist, 52*(6), 613–29.

Steele, C. M., & Aronson, J. (1995). Stereotype threat and the intellectual test performance of African Americans. *Journal of Personality and Social Psychology, 69*(5), 797–811.

Steinpreis, R. E., Anders, K. A., & Ritzke, D. (1999). The impact of gender on the review of the curricula vitae of job applicants and tenure candidates: A national empirical study. *Sex Roles, 41*(7/8), 509–28.

Stevenson, H. W., & Stigler, J. W. (1992). *The learning gap: Why our schools are failing and what we can learn from Japanese and Chinese education.* New York: Simon & Schuster.

Tierney, J. (2008, July 15). A new frontier for Title IX: Science. *New York Times.*

Trix, F., & Psenka, C. (2003). Exploring the color of glass: Letters of recommendation for female and male medical faculty. *Discourse & Society, 14*(2), 191–220.

Trower, C. A. (2008, October). Competing on culture: Academia's new strategic imperative. Unpublished presentation.

Trower, C. A., & Chait, R. P. (2002, March-April). Faculty diversity: Too little for too long. *Harvard Magazine.* Retrieved October 29, 2009, from http://harvardmagazine.com/2002/03/faculty-diversity.html.

Turner, S. L., Conkel, J. L., Starkey, M., Landgraf, R., Lapan, R. T., Siewert, J. J., Reich, A., Trotter, M. J., Neumaier, E. R., & Huang, J. (2008). Gender differences in Holland vocational personality types: Implications for school counselors. *Professional School Counseling, 11*(5), 317–26.

Turner, S. L., & Lapan, R. T. (2005). Evaluation of an intervention to increase non-traditional career interests and career-related self-efficacy among middle-school adolescents. *Journal of Vocational Behavior, 66*(3), 516–31.

Tyson, W., Lee, R., Borman, K. M., & Hanson, M. A. (2007). Science, technology, engineering, and mathematics (STEM) pathways: High school science and math coursework and postsecondary degree attainment. *Journal of Education for Students Placed at Risk, 12*(3), 243–70.

U.S. Census Bureau. (1960, 1970, 1980, 1990, & 2000). *Census of the population.* Washington, DC: Author.

U.S. Department of Education. (2006). *A test of leadership: Charting the future of U.S. higher education*. Washington, DC: Author.

U.S. Department of Education. National Center for Education Statistics. (2000). *Entry and persistence of women and minorities in college science and engineering education* (NCES 2000-601), by G. Huang, N. Taddese, & E. Walter. Washington, DC: Author.

———. (2007). *The Nation's Report Card: America's high school graduates: Results from the 2005 NAEP high school transcript study*, by C. Shettle, S. Roey, J. Mordica, R. Perkins, C. Nord, J. Teodorovic, J. Brown, M. Lyons, C. Averett, & D. Kastberg. (NCES 2007-467). Washington, DC: Government Printing Office.

U.S. Department of Labor. Bureau of Labor Statistics. (2009). *Women in the labor force: A databook* (Report 1018). Washington, DC: Author.

U.S. Government Accountability Office. (2004). *Women's participation in the sciences has increased, but agencies need to do more to ensure compliance with Title IX* (GAO-04-639). Washington, DC: Author.

———. (2006). *Science, technology, engineering and mathematics trends and the role of federal programs*: Statement of Cornelia M. Ashby, Director, Education, Workforce, and Income Security Issues (GAO-06-702T). Washington, DC: Author.

Valian, V. (1998). *Why so slow? The advancement of women.* Cambridge, MA: MIT Press.

Vasta, R., Knott, J. A., & Gaze, C. E. (1996). Can spatial training erase the gender differences on the water-level task? *Psychology of Women Quarterly, 20,* 549–567.

Vogt, C. M., Hocevar, D., & Hagedorn, L. S. (2007). A social cognitive construct validation: Determining women's and men's success in engineering programs. *The Journal of Higher Education, 78*(3), 337–64.

Voyer, D., Voyer, S., & Bryden, M. P. (1995). Magnitude of sex differences in spatial abilities: A meta-analysis and consideration of critical variables. *Psychological Bulletin, 117*(2), 250–70.

Walton, G. M., & Spencer, S. J. (2009). Latent ability: Grades and test scores systematically underestimate the intellectual ability of negatively stereotyped students. *Psychological Science, 20*(9), 1132–39.

Weinberger, C. J. (2005). Is the science and engineering workforce drawn from the far upper tail of the math ability distribution? Unpublished paper.

Wenneras, C., & Wold, A. (1997, May 22). Nepotism and sexism in peer-review. *Nature, 387,* 341–343.

WGBH Educational Foundation & Association for Computing Machinery. (2009, April). *New image for computing: Report on market research.*

Whitten, B. L., Dorato, S. R., Duncombe, M. L., Allen, P. E., Blaha, C. A., Butler, H. Z., Shaw, K. A.,Taylor, B. A. P., & Williams, B. A. (2007). What works for women in undergraduate physics and what can we learn from women's colleges. *Journal of Women and Minorities in Science and Engineering, 13*(1), 37–76.

Whitten, B. L., Foster, S. R., Duncombe, M. L., Allen, P. E., Heron, P., McCullough, L., Shaw, K. A., Taylor, B. A. P, & Zorn, H. M. (2003). What works? Increasing the participation of women in undergraduate physics. *Journal of Women and Minorities in Science and Engineering, 9,* 239–58.

———. (2004). "Like a family": What works to create friendly and respectful student faculty interactions. *Journal of Women and Minorities in Science and Engineering, 10*(3), 229–42.

Williams, D. A., & King, P. (1980, December 15). Do males have a math gene? *Newsweek, 96,* 73.

Xie, Y., & Shauman, K. A. (2003). *Women in science: Career processes and outcomes.* Cambridge, MA: Harvard University Press.

Xu, Y. J. (2008). Gender disparity in STEM disciplines: A study of faculty attrition and turnover intentions. *Research in Higher Education, 49*(7), 607–24.

Zimmerman, B. J., & Martinez-Pons, M. (1990). Student differences in self-regulated learning: Relating grade, sex, and giftedness to self-efficacy and strategy use. *Journal of Educational Psychology, 82*(1), 51–59.

AAUW Research Reports

Recent AAUW reports may be downloaded for free at www.aauw.org/research.

 Where the Girls Are: The Facts About Gender Equity in Education (2008)

 Behind the Pay Gap (2007)

 Drawing the Line: Sexual Harassment on Campus (2006)

 Tenure Denied: Cases of Sex Discrimination in Academia (2004)

 Under the Microscope: A Decade of Gender Equity Projects in the Sciences (2004)

 Women at Work (2003)

Harassment-Free Hallways: How to Stop Sexual Harassment in Schools (2002)

Hostile Hallways: Bullying, Teasing, and Sexual Harassment in School (2001)

The Third Shift: Women Learning Online (2001)

Beyond the "Gender Wars": A Conversation About Girls, Boys, and Education (2001)

¡Si, Se Puede! Yes, We Can: Latinas in School (2000)

Tech-Savvy: Educating Girls in the New Computer Age (2000)

Join Us!

❑ **YES! I want to join AAUW's community and help break through educational and economic barriers so that all women have a fair chance.**

Join online at www.aauw.org or use this form.

The AAUW community is powerful and influential:

- Our members share a strong commitment to educational and economic equity for women and girls.
- We are well known on Capitol Hill and in the civil rights and women's advocacy communities, especially in the areas of K–12, undergraduate, and graduate education.
- We have been working to advance women's equity for more than 128 years, integrating our time, our energy, and our philanthropy.

Who can join?

If you hold an associate or equivalent or higher degree from a regionally accredited college or university, you can join AAUW as an individual national member or as a member of one of AAUW's nearly 1,000 branches. Branch members also belong to the national organization.

If you are an undergraduate in a two- or four-year regionally accredited educational institution, you can join as a student affiliate of a branch or as a national student affiliate.

Join today!

Support AAUW initiatives at the national level by joining as a national member. National member dues are $49* annually.

Dues for student affiliates are $17** annually.

To become a branch member or a branch student affiliate, join at the local level. Visit www.aauw.org, e-mail connect@aauw.org, or call 800/326-AAUW (2289) to locate a branch in your area.

Please allow up to four weeks for receipt of your new member packet. AAUW does not share e-mail addresses with third parties.

❑ Occasionally AAUW's membership list is made available to carefully screened companies and organizations. Check here if you do not want your name included on the list.

*AAUW national individual membership dues for fiscal year 2010 are $49. Of that amount, $46 is tax deductible as a charitable contribution, and $3 is not deductible because it supports the AAUW Action Fund's section 501(c)(4) Lobby Corps and get-out-the-vote activities.

** The AAUW national student affiliate fee for fiscal year 2010 is $17. Of that amount, $16 is tax deductible as a charitable contribution, and $1 is not deductible because it supports the AAUW Action Fund's section 501(c)(4) Lobby Corps and get-out-the-vote activities.

Join Us!

Personal Information

Name _____

Street _____

City_____ State _____

Zip _____

Phone (H) (_____) _____

(W) (_____) _____

Fax (_____) _____

E-mail address _____

College/university _____

State _____

Degree earned/sought _____

Year graduated/anticipated graduation _____

Gender ❑ Female ❑ Male

I wish to join as an

❑ AAUW National Member ($49) M10MWSFW

❑ AAUW Student Affiliate ($17) M10SWSFW

You may qualify for FREE e-student affiliate membership. Visit https://svc.aauw.org/join/value/aauw_cu.cfm to see if your school is an AAUW partner member. If yes, contact AAUW at 800/326-2289 for your school representative.

For college/university partner memberships, visit www.aauw.org/join.

Total Enclosed $_____

Payment Information

❑ Check or money order payable to AAUW

❑ Credit card (check one): ❑ MasterCard ❑ VISA ❑ American Express ❑ Discover

Card #_ _ _ _ - _ _ _ _ - _ _ _ _ - _ _ _ _

Exp. date _____

Name on card _____

Signature _____

Today's date _____

Credit card billing address

❑ Same as above

Name _____

Street _____

City_____ State _____

Zip _____

Mail completed membership application to
AAUW, P.O. Box 96974, Washington, DC 20077-7022.

We Need Your Help.

PLEASE GIVE TODAY!

Founded in 1881, AAUW has championed the rights of women and girls in education and the workplace for more than 128 years. Hundreds of thousands of women and men have contributed their time and financial resources to help AAUW break through educational and economic barriers so that all women and girls have a fair chance. Today, our message remains as true as ever: Educating women and girls helps individuals, their families, and society. With nearly 100,000 members, 1,000 branches, and 500 college and university partners, AAUW provides a powerful voice for women and girls—in Washington, D.C., our state capitals, and our communities. AAUW's work would not be possible without generous contributions from people who share our commitment to education, passion for equity, and unwavering belief that women are an instrumental part of leadership, change, and growth. With your support, AAUW can continue its research and scholarship on issues of importance to women and girls.

❑ **Yes!** I support the work of the AAUW community. Please accept my tax-deductible
   contribution of ❑ $250   ❑ $100   ❑ $50   ❑ $25   ❑ Other (specify_____)

Name _____

Address _____   City _____

State _____   Zip _____   E-mail address _____

Payment method

❑ Check or money order payable to
   AAUW Funds

❑ Credit card (check one):   ❑ MasterCard
   ❑ VISA   ❑ American Express   ❑ Discover

Card #____-____-____-____

Exp. date _____   Today's date _____

Signature _____

Name on card _____

Billing address   ❑ Same as above

Address_____

City_____

State_____   Zip_____

Fax your completed form to 202/463-7169 (credit card payments only) or mail it to **AAUW, P.O. Box 98045, Washington, DC 20090-8045.**

To learn more about AAUW or to make contributions online, visit **www.aauw.org**.

AAUW is a 501(c)(3) corporation. Gifts are tax deductible to the extent allowed by law.

AAUW

Breaking through Barriers

By joining AAUW, you belong to a community that breaks through educational and economic barriers so that all women have a fair chance.

AAUW advances equity for women and girls through advocacy, education, and research.

In principle and in practice, AAUW values and supports diversity. There shall be no barriers to full participation in this organization on the basis of gender, race, creed, age, sexual orientation, national origin, disability, or class.